101+ RESOURCES FOR VETERANS

101+ RESOURCES FOR VETERANS

The Ultimate Resource Guide

JENNIFER HAMMOND

Published by Knowledge and Empowerment Media

Paperback: 978-1-7351797-0-4
e-book: 978-1-7351797-1-1

Printed in the United States of America

Dedication

For America's Veterans who have given
their all to serve their country.

Contents

Purpose of this Guide

Each year the Department of Veterans Affairs provides a directory of hundreds of veterans organizations, but often the information in their directory isn't well sourced and is filled with misinformation and sometimes is outright wrong. Because of this, we sought to create a book where everything from cover to cover was done by hand, by veterans for veterans. Because of our dedication to getting quality information and gratitude for your service to our country, we can now give to you our 101+ Veterans Resource Guide!

In this book you can find more than 150 organizations which cover a host of issue areas directly relating to veterans and their families. Which is why we have covered a wide array to topics and subject matter: because we know you have a lot going on too! So, please use our guide knowing that this is but the first step in a chain to get you and your family to your goals!

With this in mind, we do want you, our loyal reader to know, that despite our best efforts some groups might have changed or closed by the time you're reading this. Conversely, new groups too have opened! With all of this in mind we will also have a digital copy of this book available online at jenniferjhammond.com where you can go and see the most up to date version of our book!

From the bottom of our hearts, we hope that you are able to use this resource guide to make your life, or the life of someone you know better! Our goal in creating this book was to give our veterans and their families one more resource in their return to both civilian life but also post-service guidance. With this in mind we hope this book helps you to a better and more prosperous future, best of luck to you in all that you hope to achieve in your new, post-military world!

Acknowledgements

My gratitude and appreciation for veterans began when I was in high school and removed from the custody of my alcoholic and drug-addicted mother. I was raised by a wonderful family whose father was in the Navy, stationed in Key West, Florida. I would not have even graduated from high school if it had not been for their kindness. I also spent time in Pensacola, FL (the cradle of naval aviation), surrounded by military personnel in the classroom and community while obtaining both my BA and MPA from the University of West Florida.

I later discovered my personal connection to the military began long before that with my great-grandfather and grandfather, Thomas West Hammond I & II, both serving long careers in the Army. At one point my grandfather even taught at West Point. Also, my cousin is a retired Air Force Colonel Robert Flanagan, who grew famous for flying B-25's during the Korean War. At age 97 Col. Flanagan went to rest in peace at Arlington National Cemetery. I am especially grateful to him as he inspired me to always strive to be the best version of myself.

So, military families and veterans have helped me in countless ways and have always been a part of my life. This book is my way of giving back to those who have served around the world, helping others and keeping America free.

I'd like to thank my gracious friends Phil Randazzo, U.S. Army Colonel Cary C. Harbaugh (ret.), Colonel Colby M. Ritter, Judge Stephens, Jr., U.S. Army General Tony Thomas (ret.), Mike Warren and Ken Rochon, Jr., for their tireless dedication to helping put the best version of this book forward. I'd also like to thank my publication team, Martha Bullen and Steve Harrison, who helped to push me into putting out the best possible book for our veterans and their families! Lastly, I want to say thank you to my staff, Cate Vonich and Ryan Greene, who helped to source all of the amazing organizations that we've added into this iteration of the book!

Lastly, I'd like to take the opportunity to thank all of the veterans organizations that seek every day to do right by those who have done so much for us!

Foreword

There should be no doubt that we American Veterans are blessed to live in the greatest country on the planet. No other nation dedicates so many resources for its Veterans to assist in the health, well-being, financial support, medical care, and transition out of the military as the United States. From governmental resources at the national, state, and local community levels to a plethora of non-government entities, often in the form of benevolent organizations, there exists a vast infrastructure to provide support and assistance for nearly any issue a Veteran, family member, or Gold Star family member may need addressed.

After 41 years of active duty service in the Army, predominantly in the special operations community, I am distinctly honored to introduce this amazing guidebook to you. Designed and edited by my dear friend Jennifer Hammond, who has dedicated her life and much of her personal and professional time to advocating for the Veterans of our Nation, this resource guide will enhance your life and set you on a pathway to success. I spent the last nearly six years of my career as the Director of the Warrior Care Program for United States Special Operations Command, the program, informally known as the Care Coalition, cares for over 15,000 wounded, ill, and injured service members and their families, along with over 400 Gold Star families of our fallen special operations warriors. We refer to our program as a "coalition" because it is a coalescence of capabilities that ultimately builds the support apparatus any warrior going through the challenges of wounds, illnesses, or injuries may have to weather. Many of the organizations that are part of that coalition are represented in the pages ahead. I encourage you to find your path, identify a resource that you need, and not only avail yourself of what they (and others) offer, but get involved. Become part of the community that supports you and seek to support those that follow you into the Veteran ranks as well. The fact is the best weapon we have to address the stresses acquired in military service, deployments, and combat—including, but not limited to PTSD, depression, and anxiety disorders along with orthopedic, spinal injuries, and traumatic brain injury—is connection. Connection to the many support organizations and entities available, but most importantly, connection to each other and the greater Veteran and active-duty community. Through connection we heal, we recover, we rehabilitate, and we thrive.

Jennifer has designed this guidebook to give you a head-start and get you connected. It's not all inclusive—there are literally thousands of organizations out there—but the start-point she's providing will get you into the "network" and will allow you to springboard into a vast cornucopia of options. I encourage you to be an explorer—to be curious and quizzical—to learn about these organizations and others like them, they are amazingly interconnected and willingly assist and partner with each other which will ultimately best serve your interests. Additionally, I ask you to get and stay involved—find the services you require, but also help guide your brother and sister Veterans toward them as well. Every former service member remembers that feeling of someone covering their "six"—this guide will point you to so many that are standing by to do that for you now.

Quiet Professionals!

Colonel Cary C. Harbaugh USA (retired)

Branch Specific

"Whoever said the pen is mightier than the sword obviously never encountered automatic weapons."

–DOUGLAS MACARTHUR

AIR FORCE AID SOCIETY

Our mission is to support Airmen and enhance the Air Force mission by relieving emergency financial distress, helping Airmen's families achieve their educational goals, and improving their quality of life through proactive programs. AFAS Standard Assistance may be in the form of no-interest loan or grant. The purpose is to help stabilize the member's emergency financial situation in order to solve a problem, so the member can focus on their mission. A budget is required and payment is made to the final vendor/recipient, not the member.

Website: afas.org
Contact #: (703) 972-2650
Area of Service: National

AIR FORCE ENLISTED VILLAGE

Retirement and Senior Housing for select categories of prior service and family members. The community accepts four categories of residents: Surviving spouses of retired enlisted members of all U.S. military branches, married couples with one or both being a retired enlisted U.S. airman, married couples with one or both being a retired enlisted U.S. military member, mothers of active duty and retired enlisted U.S. airmen or, in the event of the death of the active duty enlisted U.S. Air Force sponsor, surviving spouses under the age of 55 may be admitted for a maximum of one year to meet emergency needs.

Website: afev.us
Contact #: 850-651-3766
Area of Service: Regional, Florida

AIR FORCE SERGEANTS ASSOCIATION

One of the few military associations able to lobby and provide face-to-face representation with our Nation's Congressional and Military Leaders on Capitol Hill, and within the DoD and VA. The mission of the Association is to advocate improved quality of life and economic fairness that will support the well-being of all military personnel and their families. They represent more than 100,000 military members and their families world wide.

Website: www.hqafsa.org
Contact #: 301-899-3500
Area of Service: National

COAST GUARD FOUNDATION

Founded in 1969, the Coast Guard Foundation provides education, support, and relief for the brave men and women who enforce maritime law, protect our homeland, and preserve the environment. Their founding directors were Coast Guard veterans who served together during World War II. The founders, who enjoyed successful careers after their military service, saw that the Coast Guard Academy's operate budget wasn't fully covering all of its needs, and they started the Foundation to provide funds that could make up the difference.They are committed to serving them with high quality programs and resources that enhance their service and better prepare them for duty.

Website: coastguardfoundation.org
Contact #: 860-535-0786
Area of Service: National

EOD WARRIOR FOUNDATION

The EOD Warrior Foundation (EODWF) serves the EOD community by providing financial assistance and support to Active-Duty, Reserve and National Guard, Retired and Veteran EOD technicians and their families. Their support includes financial assistance and additional services such as morale events, peer-to-peer support, educational programs, connections to resources, care of the EOD Memorial, and sustained contact with EOD warriors and their families. The Foundation believes that the EOD family is for life. Their ongoing mission is to disarm the challenges of the EOD family by providing our support with compassion and caring to every individual we serve.

Website: www.eodwarriorfoundation.org
Contact #: 850.729.2336
Area of Service: National

GREEN BERET FOUNDATION

The Green Beret Foundation serves the Army's Special Forces, our nation's most elite soldiers. They believe that the Green Berets are our nation's greatest assets. Every day, they honor their commitment to Green Berets past and present, as well as their families, by connecting them with the right resources to prosper and thrive. Because when these soldiers meet powerful opportunities, our nation's most elite soldiers become our nation's best leaders.

Website: www.greenberetfoundation.org
Contact #: (844) 287-7133
Area of Service: National

MARINE CORPS LEAGUE

Marine Corps League provides support both in material and personnel in supporting services needed by the Marine Corps. This includes funeral assistance, community involvement and scholarship opportunities. The Marine Corps League is proud to support our Marines in many areas. We have 10 Divisions covering 48 Departments, and over 1,140 Detachments in communities across the Country. In addition they support Toys for Tots efforts working with the Marine Corps Reserve and Toys for Tots Foundation to raise millions of dollars for the youth of America, collect and distribute millions of toys all across the United States.

Website: www.mclnational.org
Contact #: 703.207.9588
Area of Service: National

MARINE CORPS SCHOLARSHIP FOUNDATION

The Marine Corps Scholarship Foundation is one of the nation's oldest and largest providers of need-based scholarships to military children. For more than 55 years, they've been providing access to affordable education for the children of Marine and Navy Corpsman attending post-high school, under-graduate and career technical education programs.

Website: www.mcsf.org
Contact #: 1-703-549-0060
Area of Service: National

NAVY CLUB OF THE UNITED STATES

On 18 June 1938, at a Navy Veterans Reunion in Quincy, Illinois, the Navy Club of the United States was founded. Designed to collectively bring together the many private Navy Clubs and Navy Veteran Organizations that had sprung up across the country, and by so doing, give each member and prospective member, a powerful voice as a nationally recognized organization.

Website: navyclubusa.org
Contact #: (585) 967-4935
Area of Service: National

NAVY MUTUAL AID ASSOCIATION

The Navy Mutual Aid Association was established on July 28, 1879, during a meeting of U.S. Navy officers at the Navy Department in Washington, D.C. to better assist members of their service during financially difficult times. Today Navy Mutual assists servicemembers and their families in securing the federal benefits to which they may be legally entitled, as well as to educate servicemembers and their families on matters of financial security. Navy Mutual offers an array of insurance and other health benefits to qualified members of the military and retirement communities.

Website: www.navymutual.org
Contact #: (800) 628-6011
Area of Service: National

WOMEN'S ARMY CORPS VETERANS ASSOCIATION-ARMY WOMEN UNITED

The Women's Army Corps (WAC) Mothers Association was founded during World War II by some of the mothers of women in the Women's Army Auxiliary Corps (WAAC) which later became the Women's Army Corps. The WAC Mothers' purpose was to help both men and women by serving in hospitals and USO's, selling bonds, mending clothes, and sending comfort packages to the WACs. Today they represent women who loyally served their country in World War II, Korea, Vietnam, Grenada, Panama, Persian Gulf Bosnia and in Iraq and Afghanistan. They count among our members the former directors of the Women's Army Corps, commanders of the WAC Center and School, Officers, warrant officers, NCO's and enlisted women who were the heart of the women's tradition in the United States Army.

Website: www.armywomen.org
Contact #: 256-820-6824
Area of Service: National

Education

"Education is the most powerful weapon which you can use to change the world."

–NELSON MANDELA

ALLIED FORCES FOUNDATION

The Allied Forces Foundation is a non-profit organization established to unite wounded, ill, and injured service people and veterans as well as caregivers from US, UK, and allied nations forces in wellness and healing. Through a series of outdoor, peer-lead events that challenge the mind and body, Allied Forces Foundation provides opportunities that reinvigorate the spirit of comradeship and teamwork.

Website: www.alliedforcesfoundation.org
Contact #: 703-779-9305
Area of Service: National

AMERICAN CORPORATE PARTNERS

American Corporate Partners (ACP) is a national nonprofit organization focused on helping returning veterans and active duty spouses find their next careers through one-on-one mentoring, networking and online career advice. The organization sees the biggest issue facing our returning service members is not unemployment—it's underemployment. ACP focuses on helping veterans and active duty spouses find meaningful employment opportunities and develop long-term careers.

Website: www.acp-usa.org
Contact #: (212) 752-0700
Area of Service: National

AMERICAN DREAM U

American Dream U offers two main services for transitioning veterans: Online programs and educational workshop events. American Dream U's online programs are catered to helping veterans become successful professionals in the world of business, with breadth in courses; everything from entrepreneurship to the intricacies of setting up a LinkedIn profile. American Dream U's workshop events are fueled by the same purpose; offering unique, differentiating benefits when paired with the online courses such as networking and connecting with other veterans, as well as hearing personal success stories of post-service careers.

Website: www.americandreamu.org
Contact #: (702) 233-2366
Area of Service: National

AMVETS NATIONAL SERVICE FOUNDATION

The American Studies Center (ASC) provides professional help to veterans applying for compensation and benefits from the VA, offered at no charge. The ASC also offers thrift stores around the country for veterans. These stores offer clothes, household goods and more. Eligible veterans can apply for scholarships through the ASC website.

Website: amvetsnsf.org
Contact #: (301) 459-6181
Area of Service: National

COALITION TO SALUTE AMERICA'S HEROES

The mission of the Coalition to Salute America's Heroes is to help severely-wounded veterans and families of Operation Enduring Freedom, Operation Iraqi Freedom, and Operation New Dawn recover from their injuries and illnesses, and to inspire other organizations and the general public to participate in this effort.

Website: saluteheroes.org
Contact #: 888-447-2588
Area of Service: National

ENTREPRENEURSHIP BOOTCAMP FOR VETERANS WITH DISABILITIES

Entrepreneurship Bootcamp for Veterans with Disabilities (EBV) offers cutting edge, experiential training in entrepreneurship and small business management to post 9/11 veterans with disabilities resulting from their service to our country. The EBV is designed to open the door to business ownership for our veterans by 1) developing your skills in the many steps and activities associated with launching and growing a small business, and by 2) helping you leverage programs and services for veterans and people with disabilities in a way that furthers your entrepreneurial dreams. The EBV is designed around two central elements: a) focused, practical training in the tools and skills of new venture creation and growth, reflecting issues unique to disability and public benefits programs; and b) the establishment of a support structure for graduates of the program.

Website: www.ebvfoundation.org
Contact #: 315.443.6898
Area of Service: National

EOD WARRIOR FOUNDATION

The EOD Warrior Foundation (EODWF) serves the EOD community by providing financial assistance and support to Active-Duty, Reserve and National Guard, Retired and Veteran EOD technicians and their families. Their support includes financial assistance and additional services such as morale events, peer-to-peer support, educational programs, connections to resources, care of the EOD Memorial, and sustained contact with EOD warriors and their families. The Foundation believes that the EOD family is for life. Their ongoing mission is to disarm the challenges of the EOD family by providing our support with compassion and caring to every individual we serve.

Website: www.eodwarriorfoundation.org
Contact #: 850.729.2336
Area of Service: National

FISHER HOUSE FOUNDATION

Fisher House Foundation is best known for a network of comfort homes where military and veterans' families can stay at no cost while a loved one is receiving treatment. These homes are located at major military and VA medical centers nationwide, and, in Europe, close to the medical center or hospital it serves. Fisher

House Foundation ensures that there is never a lodging fee. Since its inception, the program has saved military and veterans' families an estimated $400+ million in out-of-pocket costs for lodging and transportation. Other Quality of Life programs include the Hero Miles and Hotels for Heroes programs, ongoing assistance to Fisher Houses, scholarships, support for continuing rehabilitation initiatives, and individual assistance to members of the military and their families during a crisis.

Website: www.fisherhouse.org
Contact #: (888) 294-8560
Area of Service: National

FLEET RESERVE ASSOCIATION

Fleet Reserve Association is first and foremost a community of the Sea Services; U.S. Navy, Marine Corps, and Coast Guard personnel. Your enlisted service in any of these branches—past or present, for a short time or for the long haul—is your passport to membership in an association that works hard for you and your family on Capitol Hill and in your local community. FRA's guiding principles are Loyalty, Protection and Service to our shipmates. The FRA offers assistance to members in managing VA applications as well as offering scholarship money for undergraduate and graduate schooling.

Website: www.fra.org/fra/Web/FRAHome
Contact #: 703-683-1400
Area of Service: National

FREEDOM ALLIANCE

The purpose of the Freedom Alliance is to better honor and support America's veterans and meet the rehabilitation needs of wounded service members, combat veterans and military families. This happens by providing families of fallen with college scholarships for our heroes' children as well as helpingAmerica's leaders shape policies that prioritize the sovereignty of our people, the security of our country, and the safety of those who fight for it.

Website: www.freedomalliance.org
Contact #: (703) 444-7940
Area of Service: National

GIVE AN HOUR

Give an Hour's mission is to develop national networks of volunteers capable of responding to both acute and chronic conditions that arise within our society. By harnessing the skill and expertise of volunteer professionals, we are able to increase the likelihood that those in need receive the support and care they deserve. Give an Hour is honored to provide help and hope to those in need through a range of services and programs. They encourage potential participants to explore their initiatives and programs to learn more about some of the important work they are doing in communities across the country.

Website: https://giveanhour.org/initiatives-and-programs/
Contact #: info@giveanhour.org
Area of Service: National

GOLD STAR WIVES OF AMERICA, INC.

Each legislative session of Congress brings up new legislation directly pertaining to military survivors. Members of Gold Star Wives appear before various House and Senate Committees on issues concerning compensation, educational benefits, medical care and other programs pertaining to the welfare of military survivors. They believe surviving spouses and dependent children need an organization dedicated solely to their needs, concerns, and welfare which can create a united and stronger together.

Website: www.goldstarwives.org
Contact #: 1-888-751-6350
Area of Service: National

INSTITUTE FOR VETERANS AND MILITARY FAMILIES

Syracuse University has a historic commitment to serving veterans and their families and the founding of the IVMF in 2011 further expands that commitment to serve across the country and beyond. Supported by a world-class advisory board and public and private partners, their professional staff delivers unique and innovative programs in career, vocations, and entrepreneurship education and training to post 9/11 veterans and active-duty military spouses, as well as tailored programs to veterans of all eras. The IVMF also provides actionable and national impacting research, policy analysis and program evaluation; and works with communities and non-profits across the nation to enhance service delivery for the 22.5 million veterans throughout the United States and their families.

Website: ivmf.syracuse.edu
Contact #: 315-443-0141
Area of Service: National

MARINE CORPS LEAGUE

Marine Corps League provides support both in material and personnel in supporting services needed by the Marine Corps. This includes funeral assistance, community involvement and scholarship opportunities. The Marine Corps League is proud to support our Marines in many areas. We have 10 Divisions covering 48 Departments, and over 1,140 Detachments in communities across the Country. In addition they support Toys for Tots efforts working with the Marine Corps Reserve and Toys for Tots Foundation to raise millions of dollars for the youth of America, collect and distribute millions of toys all across the United States.

Website: www.mclnational.org
Contact #: 703.207.9588
Area of Service: National

MARINE CORPS SCHOLARSHIP FOUNDATION

The Marine Corps Scholarship Foundation is one of the nation's oldest and largest providers of need-based scholarships to military children. For more than 55 years, they've been providing access to affordable education for the children of Marine and Navy Corpsman attending post-high school, under-graduate and career technical education programs.

Website: www.mcsf.org
Contact #: 703-549-0060
Area of Service: National

NATIONAL MILITARY FAMILY ASSOCIATION

In 1969, the Association was founded by a handful of military wives who wanted to make sure their widowed friends were properly taken care of. Two short years later, the Survivor Benefit Plan became law, and the Association has been hard at work ever since. A small, but determined, group of spouses around a kitchen table has expanded into a strong force of military families representing all ranks and services. NMFA has, for 50 years, proven to stand behind service members, their spouses, and their children. The Association is a crucial source for government officials and key decision makers when they want to understand the issues facing our families. Through the support and programs they provide, and their voice on Capitol Hill and with the Departments of Defense and Veterans Affairs, the Association always looks out for the families who stand behind the uniform and for those who serve.

Website: www.militaryfamily.org
Contact #: 703.931.6632
Area of Service: National

NATIONAL VETERANS FOUNDATION

The National Veterans Foundations provides crisis management, information and referral needs of all U.S. Veterans and their families through: management and operation of the nation's first vet-to-vet toll-free helpline for all veterans and their families. They also offer public awareness programs that shine a consistent spotlight on the needs of America's veterans in addition to providing outreach services that provide veterans and families in need with food, clothing, transportation, employment, and other essential resources.

Website: www.nvf.org
Contact #: (310) 642-0255
Area of Service: National

Navy SEAL Foundation
Since the attacks of Sept. 11, 2001, there has been an unprecedented demand for our Special Operations Forces. Never before has so much been asked of so few, from so many, for so long. Established in 2000 to serve U.S. Navy SEALs, Special Warfare Combatant-craft Crewmen, Naval Special Warfare support personnel and their families, the Navy SEAL Foundation's programs are focused on the preservation of the Naval Special Warfare force and their families. They provide a comprehensive set of programs specifically designed to improve health and welfare, build and enhance resiliency, empower and educate families and provide critical support during times of illness, injury, loss and transition.

Website: www.navysealfoundation.org
Contact #: 757.744.5326
Area of Service: National

Pat Tillman Foundation
Pat's story on the football field and the Army is well-known, but it is his principles and service that are his true legacy. Pat believed in something bigger than himself, and dedicated his life to serving it. We're dedicated to honoring that legacy. Pat's family and friends started the Pat Tillman Foundation to carry forward that legacy by giving military service members, veterans and spouses who embody those principles the educational tools and support the need to reach their fullest potential as leaders—no matter how they choose to serve. To this end they seek to unite and empower remarkable military service members, veterans and spouses as the next generation of public and private sector leaders committed to service beyond self.

Website: pattillmanfoundation.org
Contact #: (773) 360-5277
Area of Service: National

SPECIAL OPERATIONS WARRIOR FOUNDATION

Special Operations Warrior Foundation pledges to ensure full college funding to every surviving child of a special operator who loses their life in the line of duty; immediate financial burden when their loved ones are hospitalized with severe combat wounds or injuries. We fulfill this need by immediately providing a check to the service member (or their designated recipient) so the family and loved ones can be at their bedside.

Website: specialops.org
Contact #: (813) 805-9400
Area of Service: National

STUDENT VETERANS OF AMERICA

Student Veterans of America's mission is focused on empowering student veterans. They are committed to providing an educational experience that goes beyond the classroom. Through a dedicated network of more than 1,500 on-campus chapters in all 50 states and 4 countries representing more than 750,000 student veterans, SVA aims to inspire yesterday's warriors by connecting student veterans with a community of like-minded chapter leaders. Every day these passionate leaders work to provide the necessary resources, network support, and advocacy to ensure student veterans can effectively connect, expand their skills, and ultimately achieve their greatest potential.

Website: www.studentveterans.org
Contact #: (202) 223-4710
Area of Service: National

THANKS USA

ThanksUSA launched the Pathways for Patriots program to help bridge the gap between higher education and meaningful employment. In collaboration with our corporate partners, we act as a catalyst for career development opportunities that reveal military family members' unique skillsets while alleviating their common challenges.

Website: www.thanksusa.org
Contact #: (703-375-9849
Area of Service: National

VALOR RUN

For as long as this country has been fighting wars, at home or abroad, women have been injured and killed in combat zones. Valor Run honors those women, now 161, who made the ultimate sacrifice in Iraq and Afghanistan as well as the families they left behind. Please be aware that only female veterans and their children are eligible for scholarships.

Website: www.valorrun.org
Contact #: valorrun@valorrun.org
Area of Service: Regional, Virginia

VETERANS ASSOCIATION OF REAL ESTATE PROFESSIONALS

Established in 2011, the USA Homeownership Foundation, Inc. DBA Veterans Association of Real Estate Professionals (VA-REP), is a housing counseling organization dedicated to increasing sustainable homeownership, financial-literacy education, VA loan awareness, and economic opportunity for the active-military and veteran communities. While their focus is on the active-military and veteran communities, their services are also offered to eligible low-to-moderate income (LMI) families. Their doors are open to all that want to realize the American Dream of homeownership. VAREP and its members represent and work within all sectors of the real estate, housing, and financial-services industries.

Website: www.varep.net
Contact #: (951) 444-7363
Area of Service: National

Veterans Coming Home
Social entrepreneurs, researchers and academics across the country have developed powerful solutions to many returning veterans' challenges, as well as ways to support their families, employers, and communities. As communities rally to support veterans, they gain untold benefits from veterans' skills and commitment. Veterans Coming Home: Finding What Works will tell stories from communities across the the nation that are innovating and succeeding for their veterans, and close the loop to highlight the unique contributions veterans are making in return.

Website: veteranscominghome.org/education-resources
Contact #: See website for fillable form
Area of Service: National

THE JOURNEY HOME PROJECT

Often when our veterans return from their tour of service, the tolls of war have been too great to bear alone. Wars in the Middle East and other parts of the world have left some of our bravest service personnel with injuries that will affect them the rest of their lives. Some require intense rehabilitation and years of physical therapy. Other trauma cannot be seen. The horrors of war leave psychological scars that make it difficult to reenter civilian life. Many are hesitant to seek the help they need, or encounter red tape and stigma when they do reach out for help. Cutbacks to veterans' services from the federal government, combined with an increase in wartime active personnel has put a strain on health care, education and job opportunities for veterans. And so many want to help. The Journey Home Project sees as its mission connecting donors to veterans' organizations that do the most good.

Website: thejourneyhomeproject.org
Secondary Website: https://www.charliedaniels.com/vol-jam
Contact #: See website for fillable form
Area of Service: National

AMERICA'S WARRIOR PARTNERSHIP

From city to city and town to town across America, there is no one organization or platform to ensure each unique veteran is holistically supported or that each veteran service organization has access to the national resources they need. America's Warrior Partnership is filling these gaps between current veteran service organizations: bolstering efficacy, improving results, and empowering initiatives. America's Warrior Partnership is the connection that brings local veteran-centric nonprofits together through coordination and collaboration, ensuring consistent information is obtained, relevant services are provided, and national resources are utilized. We attack inefficiency and amplify the work of established nonprofits and government agencies. America's Warrior Partnership is truly a force multiplier for warrior care that enhances communities where great Americans choose to live and contribute. Our ultimate goal is to create a better quality of life for all veterans by empowering local communities to proactively and holistically serve them.

Website: americaswarriorpartnership.org
Contact #: (706) 434-1708
Area of Service: National

LEAD THE WAY

Through their Ranger Assistance Programs they address and support the ongoing needs of the Rangers and families beyond what the government can offer. They work directly with the U.S. Special Operations Care Coalition to assist U.S. Army Rangers.

Rangers are among the most disciplined and skilled Warriors in the world and they are dedicated to helping them utilize their ingrained skills by empowering them to thrive in careers and at top Universities around the country. When Rangers make the decision not to re-enlist in the Regiment after a long and successful military career, the transition back to civilian life can be challenging. Through their Transition Programs, we are committed to helping their Rangers through the reintegration process, ensuring that they achieve their goals of a rewarding and prosperous civilian life.

Website: www.leadthewayfund.org
Contact #: 516-439-5268
Area of Service: National

LEAVE NO VETERAN BEHIND

Leave No Veteran Behind (LNVB) is a national 501(c)3 non-profit organization that invests in Veterans to build better communities through employment training, transitional jobs, and our veteran educational debt relief scholarship. Leave No Veteran Behind invests in heroes who have served their country honorably and who seek to continue their service as assets in communities across America.

Website: leavenoveteranbehind.org
Contact #: 312.379.8652
Area of Service: National

Employment

"The only way to do great work is to love what you do.
If you haven't found it yet, keep looking. Don't settle."

–STEVE JOBS

AMERICAN CORPORATE PARTNERS

American Corporate Partners (ACP) is a national nonprofit organization focused on helping returning veterans and active duty spouses find their next careers through one-on-one mentoring, networking and online career advice. The organization sees biggest issue facing our returning service members is not unemployment—it's underemployment. ACP focuses on helping veterans and active duty spouses find meaningful employment opportunities and develop long-term careers.

Website: www.acp-usa.org
Contact #: (212) 752-0700
Area of Service: National

AMERICAN DREAM U

American Dream U offers two main services for transitioning veterans: Online programs and educational workshop events. American Dream U's online programs are catered to helping veterans become successful professionals in the world of business, with breadth in courses; everything from entrepreneurship to the intricacies of setting up a LinkedIn profile. American Dream U's workshop events are fueled by the same purpose; offering unique, differentiating benefits when paired with the online courses such as networking and connecting with other veterans, as well as hearing personal success stories of post-service careers.

Website: www.americandreamu.org
Contact #: (702) 233-2366
Area of Service: National

FEDS HIRE VETS

Executive Order 13518, Employment of Veterans in the Federal Government, established the Veterans Employment Initiative and OPM created its Veterans Services Office to provide strategic leadership and direction for the Initiative. Using a strategic, straightforward approach to helping the men and women who have served our country in the military find employment in the Federal Government and helping to align the talents of these individuals with key positions, Veterans Services has better positioned the Government to meet mission objectives and citizens are better served.

Website: www.fedshirevets.gov
Contact #: (202) 606-7304
Area of Service: National

HIRE HEROES USA

U.S. Army Sergeant Justin Callahan was severely injured in a landmine explosion while on patrol in Afghanistan. Back home as a patient at Walter Reed Army Medical Center, he met John Bardis. The two formed an immediate bond, and Bardis learned that Callahan's biggest concern, despite his injuries, was finding employment. After offering Callahan a job on the spot, he was inspired to create Hire Heroes USA—a nonprofit that provides free job search support to U.S. military members, veterans and military spouses. Hire Heroes USA empowers U.S. military members, veterans and military spouses to succeed in the civilian workforce.

Website: www.hireheroesusa.org
Contact #: 844-634-1520
Area of Service: National

VETERAN EMPLOYMENT CENTER (VEC)

The Department of Veterans Affairs offers the help you need to build your career and find the opportunities that are right for you. It hosts a multitude of offers regarding service connected disability and separation information. Not limited to vocational rehab and employment, educational and career counseling, and information on starting your own business. Depending on the status of discharge some family members might be eligible for the same services, check the VA website for the most up to date details on eligibility.

Website: www.va.gov/careers-employment
Contact #: 844-698-2311
Area of Service: National

VETERAN JOBS MISSION

It began in 2011 as the 100,000 Jobs Mission with 11 leading companies committed to hiring 100,000 veterans by 2020. Since then, the coalition has evolved to 200+ leading member companies that represent virtually every industry in the United States economy. The coalition has been renamed the Veteran Jobs Mission and has collectively hired more than 500,000 veterans. uilding on this momentum and reflective of the significant contributions veterans have made to the companies that have hired them, the Veteran Jobs Mission raised its goal to hiring 1 million U.S. military veterans. Beyond their ongoing search for top military talent, Veteran Jobs Mission members continue to increase their focus on retention and career development or veterans in the private sector. Members are expected to report veteran hires on a quarterly basis, attend meetings and share best practices relating to the veteran employment initiatives. The coalition is recognized as a best-in-class organization that provides opportunities for members to network with like-minded organizations and thought leaders who are making an impact.

Website: www.veteranjobsmission.com
Contact #: 315-443-0141
Area of Service: National

VETERANS ASSOCIATION OF REAL ESTATE PROFESSIONALS

Established in 2011, the USA Homeownership Foundation, Inc. DBA Veterans Association of Real Estate Professionals (VA-REP), is a housing counseling organization dedicated to increasing sustainable homeownership, financial-literacy education, VA loan awareness, and economic opportunity for the active-military and veteran communities. While their focus is on the active-military and veteran communities, their services are also offered to eligible low-to-moderate income (LMI) families. Their doors are open to all that want to realize the American Dream of homeownership.

VAREP and its members represent and work within all sectors of the real estate, housing, and financial-services industries.

Website: www.varep.net
Contact #: (951) 444-7363
Area of Service: National

VETJOBS

Casy is proud to cary on VETJOBS long-standing mission to make it easy for employers looking to hire and for all members of the military community looking for work to connect with one another. VetJobs is an anchor member of the VetJobs OCEAN (One Central Employment & Advancement Network) family of websites. They are one of the largest online resource for military-affiliated job seekers looking to attain a rewarding career and maximize their earnings. Over the past 20 years, they and their sister sites have actively helped more than 56,000 military spouses, active duty military and veterans connect to high-earning careers.

Website: vetjobs.com
Contact #: 877-838-5627
Area of Service: National

VETS IN TECH

VetsinTech (VIT) supports current and returning veterans with re-integration services, and by connecting them to the national technology ecosystem. VIT is committed to bringing together a tech-specific network, resources, and programs for our veterans interested in Education, Entrepreneurship, and Employment—the 3E's! With more than 10 offices across the continental United States, VetsinTech offers convenient opportunities to grow and expand in your post-military career. Please check their website for the most up to date offerings on employment assistance and internship opportunities.

Website: www.vetsintech.com
Contact #: See website
Area of Service: National

HELMETS TO HARDHATS

Helmets to Hardhats is designed to help military service members successfully transition back into civilian life by offering them the means to secure a quality career in the construction industry. Most career opportunities offered by the program are connected to federally-approved apprenticeship training programs. Such training is provided by the trade organizations themselves at no cost to the veteran. No prior experience is needed; in fact, most successful placements start with virtually no experience in their chosen field.

Website: https://helmetstohardhats.org/military-service-members/
Contact #: +1 (866) 741-6210
Area of Service: National

JOB OPPORTUNITIES FOR DISABLED VETERANS

Disabled person, Inc. is a 501(c)(3) charitable organization whose mission is to reduce the high unemployment rate of individuals and veterans with disabilities. They do this by offering classes teaching coding skills based on the latest tools and technologies. They additionally offer courses in microsoft, sharepoint and other digital suites. Lastly they offer coursework for in-demand skills in IT administration and cloud platform solutions.

Website: jofdav.com
Contact #: (760) 420-1269
Area of Service: National

LEAVE NO VETERAN BEHIND

Leave No Veteran Behind (LNVB) is a national 501(c)3 non-profit organization that invests in Veterans to build better communities through employment training, transitional jobs, and our veteran educational debt relief scholarship. Leave No Veteran Behind invests in heroes who have served their country honorably and who seek to continue their service as assets in communities across America.

Website: leavenoveteranbehind.org
Contact #: 312.379.8652
Area of Service: National

Entrepreneurship

"Twenty years from now you will be more disappointed by the things that you didn't do than by the ones you did do. So throw off the bowlines. Sail away from the safe harbor. Catch the trade winds in your sails. Explore. Dream. Discover."

–MARK TWAIN

ACCION LENDING

Accion is a nonprofit community lender dedicated to helping entrepreneurs generate income, build assets, create jobs and achieve financial success through business ownership. Our network serves small businesses in communities across the U.S. and is made up of three certified Community Development Financial Institutions (CDFIs). Our approach sets us apart: We work hand-in-hand with entrepreneurs to overcome every obstacle standing between them and their dream of owning a thriving business.
Website: www.us.accion.org
Contact #: (866) 245-0783
Area of Service: National

Entrepreneurship Bootcamp for Veterans with Disabilities
Entrepreneurship Bootcamp for Veterans with Disabilities (EBV) offers cutting edge, experiential training in entrepreneurship and small business management to post 9/11 veterans with disabilities resulting from their service to our country. The EBV is designed to open the door to business ownership for our veterans by 1) developing your skills in the many steps and activities associated with launching and growing a small business, and by 2) helping you leverage programs and services for veterans and people with disabilities in a way that furthers your entrepreneurial dreams. The EBV is designed around two central elements: a) focused, practical training in the tools and skills of new venture creation and growth, reflecting issues unique to disability and public benefits programs; and b) the establishment of a support structure for graduates of the program.

Website: www.ebvfoundation.org
Contact #: 315.443.6898
Area of Service: National

SMALL BUSINESS DEVELOPMENT CENTERS

The Mission of the Office of Small Business Development Centers is to promote entrepreneurship, small business growth and the US economy by providing the critical funding, oversight and support needed by the nationwide network of Small Business Development Centers.The U.S Small Business Administration (SBA) administers the Small Business Development Center Program to provide management assistance to current and prospective small business owners. SBDCs offer one-stop assistance to individuals and small businesses by providing a wide variety of information and guidance in central and easily accessible branch locations. The program is a cooperative effort of the private sector, the educational community and federal, state and local governments. It enhances economic development by providing small businesses with management and technical assistance.

Website: https://www.sba.gov/offices/headquarters/osbdc
Contact #: (800) 827-5722
Area of Service: National

VETERAN WOMEN IGNITING THE SPIRIT OF ENTREPRENEURSHIP

Veteran Women Igniting the Spirit of Entrepreneurship (V-WISE) is a premier training program in entrepreneurship and small business management operated by the Institute for Veterans and Military Families at Syracuse University. It is funded in part through a Cooperative Agreement with the U.S. Small Business Administration and the generous philanthropic support of corporate and foundation partners nationwide. V-WISE helps women veterans and female military spouses/partners find their passion and learn the business savvy skills necessary to turn an idea or start-up into a growing venture. The three-phases of the program include a 15-day online course (Phase I), 3-day entrepreneurship training event (Phase II), and ongoing mentorship, training and support opportunities for graduates launching or growing their business (Phase III).

Website: www.whitman.syr.edu/vwise
Contact #: 315.443.6898
Area of Service: National

VETERANS BUSINESS SERVICES

Veterans Business Services (VBS) represents an internet army of Veterans who look for tools, techniques and opportunities to further their entrepreneurial dreams. In our midst are thousands of Service Disabled Veterans who are qualified and best suited for self-employment. Over the last five years they have worked to persuade the Veterans Administration (VA) that a disability for some Veterans can be an awesome component for entrepreneurial success. Their goal is to continue to serve the VA Vocational Rehabilitation & Employment (VRE) for Self-Employment Program collaboration with the Small Business Administration's Office of Veteran Business Development (OVSD).

Website: www.veteransbusinessservices.us
Contact #: 503.344.6945
Area of Service: National

Family Services

"For anything worth having one must pay the price; and the price is always work, patience, love, self-sacrifice."

–JOHN BURROUGHS

CHILDREN OF FALLEN SOLDIERS RELIEF FUND

The Children of Fallen Soldiers Relief Fund was founded, October 23, 2003 during the deployment of our Founder's youngest son, 82nd Airborne Paratrooper, SPC David A. Campbell in the first wave of OIF. She founded this organization to help support surviving U.S. Military children who have lost a parent in the Afghanistan or Iraq wars by providing them with College Grants. Our College Grant Program has been expanded to include both U.S. Military children and spouses who have either lost a loved one as a result of the Afghanistan or Iraq wars or have a severely disabled parent or spouse who was injured during a deployment to either war. Our second objective is to help the surviving members of these families with financial assistance. Our goal is to award applicants of U.S. Military families that have children under the age of 18, and who are in need of assistance with housing, repairs, utilities, medical expenses, groceries, clothing, school supplies and other expenses deemed necessary in order to provide them with some support and help alleviate their need.

Website: www.cfsrf.org
Contact #: (301) 685-3421
Area of Service: National

ELIZABETH DOLE FOUNDATION

The Elizabeth Dole Foundation is the preeminent organization empowering, supporting, and honoring our nation's 5.5 million military caregivers; the spouses, parents, family members, and friends who care for America's wounded, ill, or injured veterans. Founded by Senator Elizabeth Dole in 2012, the Foundation adopts a comprehensive approach in its advocacy, working with leaders in the public, private, nonprofit and faith communities to recognize military caregivers' service and promote their well-being. To this end the Foundation seeks to strengthen and empower America's military caregivers and their families by raising public awareness, driving research, championing policy, and leading collaborations that make a significant impact on their lives.

Website: www.elizabethdolefoundation.org
Contact #: (202) 249-7171
Area of Service: National

FREEDOM ALLIANCE

The purpose of the Freedom Alliance is to better honor and support America's veterans and meet the rehabilitation needs of wounded service members, combat veterans and military families. This happens by providing families of fallen with college scholarships for our heroes' children as well as helpingAmerica's leaders shape policies that prioritize the sovereignty of our people, the security of our country, and the safety of those who fight for it.

Website: www.freedomalliance.org
Contact #: (703) 444-7940
Area of Service: National

GOLD STAR WIVES OF AMERICA, INC.

Each legislative session of Congress brings up new legislation directly pertaining to military survivors. Members of Gold Star Wives appear before various House and Senate Committees on issues concerning compensation, educational benefits, medical care and other programs pertaining to the welfare of military survivors. They believe surviving spouses and dependent children need an organization dedicated solely to their needs, concerns, and welfare which can create a united and stronger together.

Website: www.goldstarwives.org
Contact #: 1-888-751-6350
Area of Service: National

LUKE'S WINGS

Luke's Wings was founded in January 2008 by a group of compassionate individuals who observed the struggles of wounded warriors at Walter Reed Army Medical Center, now Walter Reed National Military Medical Center, in Washington, DC. From January 2008 through 2011, Luke's Wings operated as a strictly volunteer based charity. There were no salaries, no full time employees, and no office space; just passionate volunteers making a difference. However, that all changed in 2012 when sufficient funding allowed for three full time employees; ultimately growing into the organization it is today. After ten years, we now serve a long list of military medical facilities, VA medical centers and hospice facilities across the country and have provided airfare for families across all 50 states and internationally. Though far from our humble beginnings, our team of five full-time employees remain committed to maintaining a clear and obvious mission: to support the community of wounded, ill and injured service members and their loved ones with the gift of flight. Join us in our mission to keep our families flying!

Website: www.lukeswings.org
Contact #: (202) 735-5382
Area of Service: National

MILITARY CHILD EDUCATION COALITION (MCEC)

The Military Child Education Coalition goal is to ensure inclusive, quality educational opportunities for all military-connected children affected by mobility, transition, deployments and family separation. They seek to do this by shedding light on military-connected children's academic, social and emotional needs and ensuring that they're recognized, supported and appropriate responses provided. They also seek to engage with parents, and other supporting adults, are empowered with the knowledge to ensure military-connected children are college, workforce and life-ready. They believe that a strong community of partners is committed to support an environment where military-connected children thrive.

Website: www.militarychild.org
Contact #: (254) 953-1923
Area of Service: National

MILITARY WARRIORS SUPPORT FOUNDATION

Military Warriors Support Foundation's mission is to provide support and programs that facilitate a smooth and successful transition for our nation's combat wounded heroes and Gold Star families. Their programs focus on housing and homeownership, recreational activities, transportation assistance and leadership development. Through their programs, they award mortgage-free homes and payment-free vehicles to combat wounded heroes and Gold Star spouses. In addition to the home or vehicle, the families receive family and financial mentoring.

Website: militarywarriors.org
Contact #: (210) 615-8973
Area of Service: National

MISSION 22

Mission 22 is a non-profit who combats the ever-rising veteran suicide rate. Every day, more than twenty veterans are lost to suicide. Mission 22 wants to bring that number to zero. It does this with three main programs; veteran treatment programs, memorials and national awareness. Mission 22 provides treatment programs to veterans for Post-Traumatic Stress, Traumatic Brain Injury and other issues they might be facing.

Website: https://www.mission22.com/home
Contact #: (503) 908-8505
Area of Service: National

OPERATION CARE AND COMFORT (OCC) – ADOPT A MILITARY FAMILY

Americans support our Troops serving in times of war in many ways: Writing letters, mailing care packages, welcome home events, or by showing support for a deployed service member or Veteran's family. Americans open up their hearts, homes, and wallets to show that they support those who serve our country. The unique programs of Operation: Care and Comfort (OCC) (an all volunteer 501(c)(3) organization) carries on this tradition allowing caring Americans to donate their time, talent, and treasure to honor those currently serving our country and those who have served.

Website: www.occ-usa.org
Contact #: (408) 832-2929
Area of Service: National

OUR MILITARY KIDS

Our Military Kids supports children (ages 5—12th grade) of deployed National Guard and Reserve service members, as well as those of wounded veterans from all service branches, with grants that provide up to $300 for a chosen activity. Participation in these activities helps military children cope with stress and build self-confidence while their parents are recovering or serving overseas. For specific guidelines on eligibility, please see their website.

Website: www.ourmilitarykids.org
Contact #: (703) 734-6654
Area of Service: National

SALUTE, INC.

SALUTE, INC. was founded in 2003 by Will and Mary Beth Beiersdorf. Shortly after 9/11, Will (a Naval Reservist), was called to active duty and deployed to Guantanamo Bay, Cuba for thirteen months. While Will was serving in Cuba, Mary Beth and her children coped with the fear of the unknown as well as the financial and emotional strain caused by the deployment. Family, friends and their extended community stepped in to help the family. Upon Will's return, both he and Mary Beth felt the need to "give back" by helping others who were experiencing similar hardships. After sharing their vision with family and friends, SALUTE, INC. was established. SALUTE, INC. is a non-profit organization that provides financial support for our military men and women and veterans through a variety of fundraising activities.

Website: www.saluteinc.org
Contact #: 847-359-8811
Area of Service: National

TRAGEDY ASSISTANCE PROGRAM FOR SURVIVORS

TAPS offers compassionate care and resources to all those grieving the loss of a military loved one. Since 1994, TAPS has provided comfort and hope 24/7 through a national peer support network and connection to grief resources, all at no cost to surviving families and loved ones. TAPS provides a variety of programs to survivors nation and worldwide. Their National Military Survivor Seminar and Good Grief Camp has been held annually in Washington,

D.C., over Memorial Day weekend since 1994. TAPS also conducts regional survivor seminars for adults and youth programs at locations across the country, as well as retreats and expeditions around the world. Staff can get you connected to counseling in your community and help navigate benefits and resources.

Website: www.taps.org
Contact #: (800) 959-8277
Area of Service: National

UNITED THROUGH READING

United Through Reading (UTR) was founded in 1989 by the wife of a Naval flight surgeon who deployed to Vietnam leaving his infant daughter at home. When the surgeon returned home, his little girl didn't know him and he had to re-enter her life as a stranger. The founder was a reading specialist and knew firsthand the importance of exposing children to literature from birth. Thus, a powerful concept emerged. Now, 30 years later, UTR still stands strong — and proven deployment after deployment. More than two million military mothers, fathers, aunts, uncles, older siblings, and children have sustained bonds and fostered literacy by sharing stories across even the greatest distances.

Website: unitedthroughreading.org
Contact #: (858) 481-7323
Area of Service: National

VETERANS OF FOREIGN WARS NATIONAL HOME FOR CHILDREN

It was founded in 1925 as a place where the families left behind by war—mothers and children, brothers and sisters—could remain together, keeping the family circle intact even when their serviceman didn't come home. Today's families face different challenges—reintegration, post-traumatic stress, high unemployment and rehabilitation from battlefield injuries, among others—and the National Home has evolved over our decades-long history to meet those changing needs. The Veterans of Foreign Wars National Home for Children will provide children, youth and families of veterans, active-duty military and members of the VFW and its Auxiliary opportunities for growth and development in a nurturing community, and by doing so will serve as a living memorial to all veterans.

Website: www.vfwnationalhome.org
Contact #: 800-313-4200
Area of Service: National

VIETNAM VETERAN WIVES

Vietnam Veteran Wives has been created to reach out to Veterans, their spouses and families. The time has come to take a stand. Vietnam Veteran Wives was created by the wife and widow of a Vietnam Veteran, who saw a much needed area for improvement, concerning subjects such as: Benefits for spouses and children, VA Claims, PTSD issues, DIC claims, informing veterans of what benefits are available to them and to their families, after their time in service. In addition to bringing to light the fact that the VA system leaves the Spouse and families of Veterans behind when it comes to services they provide. Vietnam Veteran Wives is working hard to provide counselors for both individual and families, assisting veterans with their VA claims filing, making arrangements for transportation to local VAMC's, providing a resource for Veterans and their spouse's to turn to for guidance as to the question "where do we go from here?"

Website: www.vietnamveteranwives.org
Contact #: 509-775-8893
Area of Service: National

WOUNDED WARRIORS FAMILY SUPPORT

The mission of Wounded Warriors Family Support is to provide support to the families of those who have been wounded, injured or killed during combat operations. They see that families of our casualties suffer in many ways: some financially, some psychologically and offer aid to those who need it. For more information on events and other offerings, please see the Wounded Warriors Family Support website for additional details.

Website: www.wwfs.org
Contact #: (402) 502-7557
Area of Service: National

YELLOW RIBBON FUND, INC

The Yellow Ribbon Fund is a veteran service organization providing housing, transportation, and caregiver & family support to severely wounded, ill and injured post-9/11 servicemembers from every branch of the United States military following unexpected medical crises. Since their founding in 2005, their priority at Yellow Ribbon Fund has been to keep families together during the recovery process for wounded, ill, and injured service members. They do this by providing housing and transportation during recovery and by giving caregiver support when and where it is needed. They take our mission seriously, and it shows in the way they run their organization.

Website: yellowribbonfund.org
Contact #: 240-223-1180
Area of Service: National

HOMES FIT FOR HEROES

Our Homes Fit for Heroes program provides free apartments to wounded special operations warriors and their families. The purpose of our program is to go above and beyond what is provided by our government and treat these individuals with the respect and honor they deserve. We also provide housing assistance to former service members whose injuries prevented them from returning to active duty.

Website: homesfitforheroes.net
Contact #: (201) 258-1977
Area of Service: National

Financial Services

"A nickel ain't worth a dime anymore."

–YOGI BERRA

ACCION LENDING

Accion is a nonprofit community lender dedicated to helping entrepreneurs generate income, build assets, create jobs and achieve financial success through business ownership. Our network serves small businesses in communities across the U.S. and is made up of three certified Community Development Financial Institutions (CDFIs). Our approach sets us apart: We work hand-in-hand with entrepreneurs to overcome every obstacle standing between them and their dream of owning a thriving business.

Website: www.us.accion.org
Contact #: (866) 245-0783
Area of Service: National

AIR FORCE AID SOCIETY

Our mission is to support Airmen and enhance the Air Force mission by relieving emergency financial distress, helping Airmen's families achieve their educational goals, and improving their quality of life through proactive programs. AFAS Standard Assistance may be in the form of no-interest loan or grant. The purpose is to help stabilize the member's emergency financial situation in order to solve a problem, so the member can focus on their mission. A budget is required and payment is made to the final vendor/recipient, not the member.

Website: afas.org
Contact #: (703) 972-2650
Area of Service: National

AIR FORCE SERGEANTS ASSOCIATION

One of the few military associations able to lobby and provide face-to-face representation with our Nation's Congressional and Military Leaders on Capitol Hill, and within the DoD and VA. The mission of the Association is to advocate improved quality of life and economic fairness that will support the well-being of all military personnel and their families. They represent more than 100,000 military members and their families world wide.

Website: www.hqafsa.org
Contact #: 301-899-3500
Area of Service: National

ARMED FORCES FAMILIES FOUNDATION

The Armed Forces Families Foundation is a 501(c)(3) non-profit organization made up of volunteers from many communities across the United States. Whos commitment has led to the completion of multiple projects that will benefit the families of our service men and women for years to come. Their focus is primarily on areas of significant need which often fall outside the tight budget constraints of the military and its family support organizations.

Website: www.aerhq.org
Contact #: 855-627-1726
Area of Service: National

COALITION TO SALUTE AMERICA'S HEROES

The mission of the Coalition to Salute America's Heroes is to help severely-wounded veterans and families of Operation Enduring Freedom, Operation Iraqi Freedom, and Operation New Dawn recover from their injuries and illnesses, and to inspire other organizations and the general public to participate in this effort.

Website: saluteheroes.org
Contact #: 888-447-2588
Area of Service: National

COAST GUARD FOUNDATION

Founded in 1969, the Coast Guard Foundation provides education, support, and relief for the brave men and women who enforce maritime law, protect our homeland, and preserve the environment. Their founding directors were Coast Guard veterans who served together during World War II. The founders, who enjoyed successful careers after their military service, saw that the Coast Guard Academy's operate budget wasn't fully covering all of its needs, and they started the Foundation to provide funds that could make up the difference.They are committed to serving them with high quality programs and resources that enhance their service and better prepare them for duty.

Website: coastguardfoundation.org
Contact #: 860-535-0786
Area of Service: National

COMBAT SOLDIERS RECOVERY FUND

The Combat Soldiers Recovery Fund (CSRF) makes it possible for you to help our country's severely wounded soldiers in a personal and meaningful way. CSRF is unique in that 100% of your donation goes directly to recovering soldiers. With your donation, small or large, you can bring sunlight into a hospital room and into the life of a war-wounded soldier. By helping with an expense that they otherwise simply would not be able to afford, your contribution provides immediate relief and hope. Garland Miller, a business-owner in Chevy Chase, Maryland, founded CSRF in 2004. Wanting to help wounded soldiers, she discovered that a charitable donation to other organizations supports their overhead, rather than 100% of the recipient's needs. Ms. Miller donates her time and the resources of her bookkeeping firm, Schoolfield & Associates, Inc., so that every dollar of every donation goes to recovering soldiers. Other professionals from the community also donate their time and expertise to make CSRF possible.

Website: www.combatsoldiersrecoveryfund.org
Contact #: 301.986.4851
Area of Service: Regional–Washington DC Area

DAVID LYNCH FOUNDATION

In 2005, we started the David Lynch Foundation for Consciousness-Based Education and World Peace to ensure that every child anywhere in the world who wanted to learn to meditate could do so. Now, the Foundation is actively teaching TM to adults and children in countries everywhere. How are we able to do it? Because of the generosity of foundations and philanthropists and everyday people who want to ease the suffering of others—and who want to help create a better world. If you don't already meditate, take my advice: Start. It will be the best decision you ever make.

Website: https://www.davidlynchfoundation.org/veterans.html
Contact #: 212-644-9880
Area of Service: National

GREEN BERET FOUNDATION

The Green Beret Foundation serves the Army's Special Forces, our nation's most elite soldiers. They believe that the Green Berets are our nation's greatest assets. Every day, they honor their commitment to Green Berets past and present, as well as their families, by connecting them with the right resources to prosper and thrive. Because when these soldiers meet powerful opportunities, our nation's most elite soldiers become our nation's best leaders.

Website: www.greenberetfoundation.org
Contact #: (844) 287-7133
Area of Service: National

NAVY-MARINE CORPS RELIEF SOCIETY

The mission of the Navy-Marine Corps Relief Society is to provide, in partnership with the Navy and Marine Corps, financial, educational, and other assistance to members of the Naval Service of the United States, eligible family members, and survivors when in need; and to receive and manage funds to administer these programs. They do this by operating as a volunteer service organization which uses both financial and non-financial resources to identify solutions to meet emerging needs. They help clients improve personal financial skills and encourage individual financial responsibility.

Website: www.nmcrs.org
Contact #: (800)-654-8364
Area of Service: National

SALUTE, INC.

SALUTE, INC. was founded in 2003 by Will and Mary Beth Beiersdorf. Shortly after 9/11, Will (a Naval Reservist), was called to active duty and deployed to Guantanamo Bay, Cuba for thirteen months. While Will was serving in Cuba, Mary Beth and her children coped with the fear of the unknown as well as the financial and emotional strain caused by the deployment. Family, friends and their extended community stepped in to help the family. Upon Will's return, both he and Mary Beth felt the need to "give back" by helping others who were experiencing similar hardships. After sharing their vision with family and friends, SALUTE, INC. was established. SALUTE, INC. is a non-profit organization that provides financial support for our military men and women and veterans through a variety of fundraising activities.

Website: www.saluteinc.org
Contact #: 847-359-8811
Area of Service: National

SOLDIERS' ANGELS

Soldiers' Angels has a 96.5% Efficiency Rating and has become one of the highest rated nonprofits in the country. The mission of Soldiers' Angels is to provide aid and comfort to the men and women of the United States Army, Marines, Navy, Air Force, Coast Guard, their families, and a growing veteran population. Thousands of Soldiers' Angels "Angel" volunteers assist veterans, wounded, deployed personnel, and their families in a variety of unique and effective ways. In 2018 alone, Soldiers' Angels provided over $25 million in aid to over 515,000 service members, veterans, wounded heroes, and military families. Through the Deployed Support Programs, combat deployed service members were supported with 28,659 care packages and 177,307 letters. The Veteran Support Program served over 24,600 veterans with food assistance and handed out over 39,995 items bedside to patients in VA Hospitals across the country. Through the seasonal holiday Adopt-A-Family program, Soldiers' Angels volunteers "adopted" 1,637 military families, that included 2,882 military children. New and expectant spouses of combat deployed as well as active-duty female service members were provided 1,165 baby boxes to help them welcome their new bundles of joy. Soldiers' Angels volunteers are the heart of the organization and logged over 164,524 volunteer hours just in 2018!

Website: soldiersangels.org
Contact #: 210-629-0020
Area of Service: National

SUPPORT THE ENLISTED PROJECT

Support The Enlisted Project (STEP) builds financial self-sufficiency among junior active duty enlisted service members and recently discharged enlisted Veterans and their families in Southern California facing financial crisis through counseling, education and grants. They aim to do this by being relevant, reliable and responsive to the needs of their local military community. STEP's vision is to change the lives of military families and Veterans that we serve by helping them achieve financial self-sufficiency.

Website: www.stepsocal.org
Contact #: (858) 695-6810
Area of Service: Regional–Southern California

Government

"The government is us; we are the government, you and I."

–26TH PRESIDENT THEODORE ROOSEVELT

MONTGOMERY GI BILL & SELECTED RESERVE (MGIB-SR)

The Montgomery GI Bill is for active duty members who enroll and pay $100 per month for 12 months and are then entitled to receive a monthly education benefit once they have completed a minimum service obligation. The Reservist rider covers reservists with a six-year obligation in the Selected Reserve who are actively drilling.

Website: www.benefits.va.gov/gibill/mgib_sr.asp
Contact #: 844-698-2311
Area of Service: National

SPECIAL HOUSING ADAPTATION (SHA) GRANT

The Specially Adapted Housing (SAH) program offers grants to Servicemembers and veterans with certain severe service-connected disabilities. The grants assist with building, remodeling or purchasing an adapted home.

Website:
www.benefits.va.gov/homeloans/adaptedhousing.asp
Contact #: 844-698-2311
Area of Service: National

STATE VETERANS HOME CONSTRUCTION GRANT PROGRAM

The VA State Veterans Home Construction Grant Program is a partnership between the U.S. Department of Veterans Affairs (VA) and the States to construct, renovate, or repair State owned and operated nursing homes, domiciliaries, and/or adult day health care facilities.

Website: www.cfm.va.gov/til/grants.asp
Contact #: 844-698-2311
Area of Service: National

U.S. DEPARTMENT OF VETERANS AFFAIRS

The Department of Veterans Affairs was created to provide veterans the world-class benefits and services they have earned–and to do so by adhering to the highest standards of compassion, commitment, excellence, professionalism, integrity, accountability, and stewardship.

Website: www.va.gov
Contact #: 844-698-2311
Area of Service: National

USDA FARMER PROGRAM

USDA provides affordable multi-family rental housing in rural areas by financing projects geared for low-income, elderly and disabled individuals and families as well as domestic farm laborers. They extend their reach by guaranteeing loans for affordable rental housing designed for low to moderate-income residents in rural areas and towns.

Website: https://www.rd.usda.gov/programs-services/all-programs/multi-family-housing-programs
Contact #: N/A
Area of Service: National

VA HOME MORTGAGES

The Department of Veterans Affairs (VA) helps service members, veterans, and eligible surviving spouses become homeowners. As part of their mission to serve you, they provide a home loan guarantee benefit and other housing-related programs to help you buy, build, repair, retain, or adapt a home for your own personal occupancy. VA Home Loans are provided by private lenders, such as banks and mortgage companies. VA guarantees a portion of the loan, enabling the lender to provide you with more favorable terms.

Website: https://www.benefits.va.gov/homeloans/
Contact #: 844-698-2311
Area of Service: National

VA'S HOMELESS PROVIDERS GRANT AND PER DIEM PROGRAM

The Department of Veterans Affairs (VA) Homeless Providers Grant and Per Diem Program is offered annually (as funding permits) by the Department of Veterans Affairs Health Care for Homeless Veterans (HCHV) Programs to fund community agencies providing services to homeless Veterans. The purpose is to promote the development and provision of supportive housing and/or supportive services with the goal of helping homeless Veterans achieve residential stability, increase their skill levels and/or income, and obtain greater self-determination.

Website: www.va.gov/homeless/gpd.asp
Contact #: 844-698-2311
Area of Service: National

VETERAN PENSION PROGRAM & SURVIVOR PENSION PROGRAM

Survivors Pension, which was formerly referred to as Death Pension, is a tax-free benefit payable to a low-income, unremarried surviving spouse or unmarried child(ren) of a deceased Veteran with wartime service.

Website: www.benefits.va.gov/pension/spousepen.asp
Contact #: 844-698-2311
Area of Service: National

VETERANS EDUCATION ASSISTANCE PROGRAM (VEAP)

Veterans Educational Assistance Program is available if you elected to make contributions from your military pay to participate in this education benefit program. The government matches your contributions on a 2-for-1 basis. Assistance may be used for college degree and certificate programs, technical or vocational courses, flight training, apprenticeships or on-the-job training, high-tech training, licensing and certification tests, entrepreneurship training, certain entrance examinations, and correspondence courses. In certain circumstances, remedial, deficiency, and refresher training may also be available. Check the VEAP website for the most up to date offerings and eligibility requirements.

Website: www.benefits.va.gov/gibill/veap.asp
Contact #: 844-698-2311
Area of Service: National

STATE VETERANS AFFAIRS BUREAU'S

Alabama
https://va.alabama.gov/

Alaska
http://veterans.alaska.gov/

Arizona
https://dvs.az.gov/

Arkansas
http://www.veterans.arkansas.gov/

California
https://www.calvet.ca.gov/

Colorado
https://www.colorado.gov/pacific/vets

Connecticut
https://portal.ct.gov/DVA

Delaware
https://vets.delaware.gov/

Florida
http://floridavets.org/

Georgia
https://veterans.georgia.gov/

Hawaii
http://dod.hawaii.gov/ovs/

Idaho
http://www.veterans.idaho.gov/

Illinois
https://www2.illinois.gov/veterans/Pages/default.aspx

Indiana
https://www.in.gov/dva/

Iowa
https://va.iowa.gov/

Kansas
https://kcva.ks.gov/

Kentucky
https://veterans.ky.gov/Pages/default.aspx

Louisiana
https://www.vetaffairs.la.gov/

Maine
https://www.maine.gov/veterans/

Maryland
https://veterans.maryland.gov/

Massachusetts
https://www.mass.gov/orgs/massachusetts-department-of-veterans-services

Michigan
https://www.michiganveterans.com/

Minnesota
https://mn.gov/mdva/homes/minneapolis/

Mississippi
https://www.msva.ms.gov/

Missouri
https://mvc.dps.mo.gov/index.php

Montana
http://montanadma.org/montana-veterans-affairs

Nebraska
https://veterans.nebraska.gov/

Nevada
https://veterans.nv.gov/

New Hampshire
https://www.nh.gov/nhveterans/

New Jersey
https://www.nj.gov/military/

New Mexico
http://www.nmdvs.org/

New York
https://veterans.ny.gov/

North Carolina
https://www.milvets.nc.gov/

North Dakota
http://www.nd.gov/veterans/

Ohio
http://dvs.ohio.gov/main/home.html

Oklahoma
https://odva.ok.gov/

Oregon
https://www.oregon.gov/odva/Pages/default.aspx

Pennsylvania
https://www.dmva.pa.gov/veteransaffairs/Pages/default.aspx

Rhode Island
http://www.vets.ri.gov/

South Carolina
http://va.sc.gov/

South Dakota
https://vetaffairs.sd.gov/

Tennessee
https://www.tn.gov/veteran.html

Texas
https://www.tvc.texas.gov/

Utah
https://veterans.utah.gov/

Vermont
https://veterans.vermont.gov/

Virginia
https://www.dvs.virginia.gov/

Washington
https://www.dva.wa.gov/

West Virginia
https://veterans.wv.gov/Pages/default.aspx

Wisconsin
https://dva.wi.gov/Pages/Home.aspx

Wyoming
https://www.wyomilitary.wyo.gov/veterans/

Washington D.C.
https://ova.dc.gov/

Housing

"A house is made of bricks and beams.
A home is made of hopes and dreams."

–ANONYMOUS

AIR FORCE ENLISTED VILLAGE

Retirement and Senior Housing for select categories of prior service and family members. The community accepts four categories of residents: Surviving spouses of retired enlisted members of all U.S. military branches, married couples with one or both being a retired enlisted U.S. airman, married couples with one or both being a retired enlisted U.S. military member, mothers of active duty and retired enlisted U.S. airmen or, in the event of the death of the active duty enlisted U.S. Air Force sponsor, surviving spouses under the age of 55 may be admitted for a maximum of one year to meet emergency needs.

Website: afev.us
Contact #: 850-651-3766
Area of Service: Regional, Florida

BUILDING HOMES FOR HEROES

Homes for Heroes (HoH) was founded after the September 11th attack to better support veterans returning from conflicts overseas. Since its inception HoH has created more than 225 homes for veterans. Building Homes for Heroes has grown to become a nationwide partnership of communities and corporations working together to make our country a better place by serving our nation's heroes.

Website: www.buildinghomesforheroes.org
Contact #: (516) 684-9220
Area of Service: National

FISHER HOUSE FOUNDATION

Fisher House Foundation is best known for a network of comfort homes where military and veterans' families can stay at no cost while a loved one is receiving treatment. These homes are located at major military and VA medical centers nationwide, and, in Europe, close to the medical center or hospital it serves. Fisher House Foundation ensures that there is never a lodging fee. Since its inception, the program has saved military and veterans' families an estimated $400+ million in out-of-pocket costs for lodging and transportation. Other Quality of Life programs include the Hero Miles and Hotels for Heroes programs, ongoing assistance to Fisher Houses, scholarships, support for continuing rehabilitation initiatives, and individual assistance to members of the military and their families during a crisis.

Website: www.fisherhouse.org
Contact #: (888) 294-8560
Area of Service: National

GARY SINISE FOUNDATION

The Gary Sinise Foundation was established under the philanthropic direction of a forty-year advocate for our nation's defenders, actor Gary Sinise. Each of the Foundation's programs originated from Gary's personal relationships with our nation's service community and a wide range of nonprofits he had supported for decades. Ever aware of the gaps of care these deserving heroes often encounter, he was inspired to serve them—always giving a little more. With the creation of the Gary Sinise Foundation, his crusade now supports all those who sacrifice on our behalf: active duty, veterans, first responders, and their loved ones. Each program shows appreciation for America's heroes through entertainment, family support, and acts of gratitude. At the Gary Sinise Foundation, they serve our nation by honoring our defenders, veterans, first responders, their families, and those in need. They do this by creating and supporting unique programs designed to entertain, educate, inspire, strengthen, and build communities.

Website: www.garysinisefoundation.org
Contact #: (888) 708-7757
Area of Service: National

HABITAT FOR HEROES

The goals of the Habitat for Heroes program are to provide current and former military members with the opportunity to engage in their community by volunteering and to provide former military members access to quality affordable housing. Habitat is always accepting applications for former military members or veterans interested in becoming Habitat homeowners. Please review the information provided below about the program qualifications. A former military member or veteran is defined as a "person who served in the active military, naval or air service, and who was discharged or released under conditions other than dishonorable."

Website: https://www.habitatpgw.org/habitat-for-heroes.html
Contact #: 757-596-5553 ext 2
Area of Service: National

HELPING A HERO

Helping a Hero seeks to empower our severely wounded veterans returning from service in the War on Terror, primarily by partnering with the wounded hero to provide specially adapted homes to reintegrate them into their community. The organization was founded in 2006 and provides support for military personnel severely injured in the war on terror. Their principal activity is to provide specially adapted homes for qualifying service members through partnerships made with the builders, developers, communities, and the veteran. Helping a Hero strives to engage the community in providing services and resources for their wounded heroes and their families. Additionally, Helping a Hero provides additional support programs such as marriage retreats, caregiver retreats, recreational activities, emotional support, and financial support.

Website: www.helpingahero.org
Contact #: (888) 786-9531
Area of Service: National

HOMES FOR OUR TROOPS

Homes For Our Troops (HFOT) is a publicly funded nonprofit organization that builds and donates specially adapted custom homes nationwide for severely injured post-9/11 Veterans, to enable them to rebuild their lives. Most of these Veterans have sustained injuries including multiple limb amputations, partial or full paralysis, and/or severe traumatic brain injury (TBI). These homes restore some of the freedom and independence our Veterans sacrificed while defending our country, and enable them to focus on their family, recovery, and rebuilding their lives. Since its inception in 2004, nearly 90 cents out of every dollar spent has gone directly to our program services for Veterans. HFOT builds these homes where the Veteran chooses to live, and continues its relationship with the Veterans after home delivery to assist them with rebuilding their lives. Since 2004, HFOT has built 290 specially adapted homes nationwide. Our goal is to build a home for every Veteran who qualifies for one of our specially adapted homes.

Website: www.hfotusa.org
Contact #: 866-787-6677
Area of Service: National

HUD-VASH VOUCHERS

The Departments of Housing and Urban Development-Veterans Affairs Supportive Housing (HUD-VASH) program combines Housing Choice Voucher (HCV) rental assistance for homeless Veterans with case management and clinical services provided by the Department of Veterans Affairs (VA). VA provides these services for participating Veterans at VA medical centers (VAMCs) and community-based outreach clinics.

Website: https://www.hud.gov/program_offices/public_indian_housing/programs/hcv/vash
Contact #: (202) 708-1112
Area of Service: National

MILITARY WARRIORS SUPPORT FOUNDATION

Military Warriors Support Foundation's mission is to provide support and programs that facilitate a smooth and successful transition for our nation's combat wounded heroes and Gold Star families. Their programs focus on housing and homeownership, recreational activities, transportation assistance and leadership development. Through their programs, they award mortgage-free homes and payment-free vehicles to combat wounded heroes and Gold Star spouses. In addition to the home or vehicle, the families receive family and financial mentoring.

Website: militarywarriors.org
Contact #: (210) 615-8973
Area of Service: National

NEW DIRECTIONS FOR VETERANS

Since 1992, New Directions for Veterans (NDVets) has provided comprehensive services to thousands of veterans in Los Angeles County. Founded by two formerly homeless Vietnam veterans and a local advocate for homeless persons, NDVets initially operated out of a five-bedroom home serving eight homeless Vietnam War veterans. We now operate 2 Transitional Housing Programs for veterans on the street in need of housing and 6 Permanent Supportive Housing (PSH) facilities in Los Angeles County, along with 6 additional sites that will finish construction by 2020.

Website: ndvets.org
Contact #: (310) 914-5966
Area of Service: National

HOMES FIT FOR HEROES

Our Homes Fit for Heroes program provides free apartments to wounded special operations warriors and their families. The purpose of our program is to go above and beyond what is provided by our government and treat these individuals with the respect and honor they deserve. We also provide housing assistance to former service members whose injuries prevented them from returning to active duty.

Website: homesfitforheroes.net
Contact #: (201) 258-1977
Area of Service: National

OPERATION HOMEFRONT

Operation Homefront is a national nonprofit whose mission is to build strong, stable, and secure military families so they can thrive — not simply struggle to get by — in the communities they have worked so hard to protect. For over fifteen years, we have provided programs that offer: RELIEF (through Critical Financial

Assistance and transitional housing programs), RESILIENCY (through permanent housing and caregiver support services) and RECURRING FAMILY SUPPORT programs and services throughout the year that help military families overcome the short-term bumps in the road so they don't become long-term chronic problems. Operation Homefront has consistently earned high ratings from leading charity rating services, including Charity Navigator, which gave OH 4 Stars for 11 consecutive years for superior service and accountability. At Operation Homefront, 92 percent of expenditures goes directly toward delivering programs and services to the military families who need it most.

Website: www.operationhomefront.net
Contact #: (210) 659-7756
Area of Service: National

OPERATION RENEWED HOPE FOUNDATION

Operation Renewed Hope Foundation's (ORHF) mission is to provide quality housing and supportive services to our Nation's homeless Veterans. They provide a range of services assisting Veterans and breaking their cycle of homelessness or preventing Veterans from becoming homeless. works with landlords and rental agencies throughout the metro DC area finding suitable places for Veterans and their families, thus providing a stable housing environment. ORHF partners with community organizations and citizens in the tri-state area, picking up donated furniture and household items delivering directly to the Veteran's home.

Website: www.operationrenewedhopefoundation.org
Contact #: (703)-887-8117
Area of Service: Regional–Washington D.C. metro area

SWORDS TO PLOWSHARES

Founded in 1974 by veterans, Swords to Plowshares is a community-based not-for-profit 501(c)(3) organization that provides needs assessment and case management, employment and training, housing, and legal assistance to roughly 3,000 veterans in the San Francisco Bay Area each year. We also advocate on behalf of veterans and provide community education for over 1,500 first responders, employers, social workers, attorneys, and other professionals who engage with veterans. The Department of Veterans Affairs provides healthcare and benefits to a percentage of veterans, but depends on community partners, including Swords to Plowshares, to fill in the gaps and meet the needs of those who have served. Our community comes together to deliver local, comprehensive services to meet the needs of our veterans.

Website: www.swords-to-plowshares.org
Contact #: (415) 252-4788
Area of Service: Regional–California: The Bay Area

USA CARES

USA Cares is committed to its mission to provide financial and advocacy assistance to post-9/11 active duty U.S. military service personnel, veterans and their families. USA Cares was launched through a grassroots partnership between WAVE-3 TV in Louisville, KY, the Mid-South Division of Kroger Food Stores, and the Association of the United States Army Fort Knox Chapter. The organization was dubbed Kentuckiana Cares, with a goal to raise funds to help military families in financial crisis through the sale of "Support Our Troops" yard signs. In October 2003, in response to the increasing number of requests for assistance, Kentuckiana Cares evolved into what is now USA Cares, a national non-profit organization that has assisted thousands of veterans and military families facing hardships related to service.

Website: usacares.org
Contact #: 800-773-0387
Area of Service: National

VETERANS OF FOREIGN WARS NATIONAL HOME FOR CHILDREN

It was founded in 1925 as a place where the families left behind by war—mothers and children, brothers and sisters—could remain together, keeping the family circle intact even when their serviceman didn't come home. Today's families face different challenges—reintegration, post-traumatic stress, high unemployment and rehabilitation from battlefield injuries, among others—and the National Home has evolved over our decades-long history to meet those changing needs. The Veterans of Foreign Wars National Home for Children will provide children, youth and families of veterans, active-duty military and members of the VFW and its

Auxiliary opportunities for growth and development in a nurturing community, and by doing so will serve as a living memorial to all veterans.

Website: www.vfwnationalhome.org
Contact #: 800-313-4200
Area of Service: National

VETERANS SUPPORT FOUNDATION

In cooperation with Vietnam Veterans of America, VSF supports Service Officer Programs that help veterans with service-incurred disabilities obtain the health and financial compensation they've earned. Recently, the Veterans Support Foundation provided nearly $184,000 in grants to Service Officer Programs in 15 states. Collectively, these programs secure many millions of dollars annually in compensation for veterans.

Website: www.vsf-usa.org
Contact #: 800-882-1316 ext 126
Area of Service: National

OPERATION FINALLY HOME

Operation FINALLY HOME was established in 2005 as a nonpartisan/nonprofit 501(c)(3) organization and has already had a significant impact across the country. To date, we have over 250 home projects completed or in planning in 33 states providing custom-built, mortgage-free homes to America's military heroes and the widows of the fallen, those who have worn America's uniform and sacrificed so much to defend our freedoms and values. While we are very proud of the work we have been able to do, we are keenly aware that there is much more to be done.

Website: operationfinallyhome.org
Contact #: (806) 441-5712
Area of Service: National

HOMES FIT FOR HEROES

Our Homes Fit for Heroes program provides free apartments to wounded special operations warriors and their families. The purpose of our program is to go above and beyond what is provided by our government and treat these individuals with the respect and honor they deserve. We also provide housing assistance to former service members whose injuries prevented them from returning to active duty.

Website: homesfitforheroes.net
Contact #: (201) 258-1977
Area of Service: National

Places of Interest

"It is good people who make good place."
–ANNA SEWELL

ADMIRAL NIMITZ FOUNDATION

To provide national leadership in articulating the history and lessons learned from the Pacific-Asiatic Theater of Operations during World War II and to offer educational platforms for their application to current and future national security issues, to continue to preserve the legacy of Fleet Admiral Chester W. Nimitz and the men and women who served in this theater of operations, and to facilitate programs that honor and support all veterans, past and present.

Website: www.pacificwarmuseum.org
Contact #: (800) 997-8600
Area of Service: Regional–Texas

THE AMERICAN VETERANS DISABLED FOR LIFE MEMORIAL

A memorial in Washington D.C. to honor service members who have suffered injury in service to our country.

Website: avdlm.org
Contact #: (877) 426-2838
Area of Service: Regional–Washington DC Area

JAPANESE AMERICAN WAR MEMORIAL

The memorial is dedicated to preserving the legacy of the Japanese Americans during World War II by honoring their heroic military service and patriotism while educating the public of their unjust incarceration and sacrifices.

Website: www.njamemorial.org
Contact #: (202) 503-9589
Area of Service: Regional–Washington DC Area

MEDAL OF HONOR MUSEUM

The museum will offer an experience that draws personal and emotional connections to Medal of Honor recipients and their stories, while shedding light on the wars in which they fought and the ideals that the Medal of Honor represents. Visitors will come to understand the meaning and price of freedom—and appreciate the virtue of putting service above self. The National Medal of Honor Museum will also include an education center aimed at character development in our nation's youth. A critical part of our mission will be to use the stories of our Medal of Honor recipients to inspire young people, and motivate them to be their best selves.

Website: mohmuseum.org
Contact #: (843) 284-8030
Area of Service: Regional–South Carolina

NATIONAL WORLD WAR II MUSEUM

The National WWII Museum tells the story of the American Experience in the war that changed the world-why it was fought, how it was won, and what it means today-so that all generations will understand the price of freedom and be inspired by what they learn.

Website: www.nationalww2museum.org
Contact #: (504) 528-1944
Area of Service: Regional, Louisiana

U.S. NAVY MEMORIAL FOUNDATION

Honor, Recognize, and celebrate the men and women of the Sea Services, past, present, and future; and to Inform the public about their service.

Website: www.navymemorial.org
Contact #: (202) 380-0710
Area of Service: Regional–Washington DC Area

VIETNAM VETERANS MEMORIAL FUND

Authorized by the U.S. Congress in 1980 to build a national memorial dedicated to all who served with the U.S. armed forces in the Vietnam War. Incorporated on April 27, 1979 by a group of veterans led by Jan C. Scruggs, the organization sought a tangible symbol of recognition from the American people for those who served in the war.

Website: www.vvmf.org
Contact #: (202) 393-0090
Area of Service: Regional–Washington DC Area

9/11 MEMORIAL & MUSEUM

The 9/11 Memorial & Museum is the country's principal institution concerned with exploring 9/11, documenting its impact, and examining its continuing significance. Honoring those who were killed in the 2001 and 1993 attacks is at the heart of our mission.

Website: 911memorial.org
Contact #: 212-312-8800
Area of Service: Regional, NYC

Physical and Mental Wellness

"We need to learn to set our course by the stars, not by the lights of every passing ship."

–OMAR BRADLEY

ADAPTIVE SPORTS FOUNDATION

The ASF's Warriors in Motion® (WIM) program provides participating injured United States servicemen and women with a basic knowledge and practice of wellness and the importance of lifelong healthy living. Each event includes adaptive sports and nutrition instruction as well as other healthful practices such as yoga, and stress reduction techniques. Over the course of the event, there is also time for the participants to connect with each other. We view the time that veterans spend together as an essential part of their healing. All Warriors in Motion programs are goal oriented and empower warrior, to take charge of their own fitness and wellness.

Website: www.adaptivesportsfoundation.org
Contact #: (518) 734-5070
Area of Service: National

ALLIED FORCES FOUNDATION

Allied Forced Foundation, non-profit organization, was established to unite wounded, ill, and injured service people and veterans as well as caregivers from US, UK, and allied nations forces in wellness and healing. Through a series of outdoor, peer-lead events that challenge the mind and body, Allied Forces Foundation provides opportunities that reinvigorate the spirit of comradeship and teamwork and instill a renewed sense of purpose with the Veteran.

Website: www.alliedforcesfoundation.org
Contact #: 703-779-9305
Area of Service: National

CATHOLIC WAR VETERANS, USA

The Catholic War Veterans received an Apostolic Blessing from Pope Pius XI in 1935 and a Congressional Charter from President Reagan in 1984. With Posts throughout the country, the CWV and their Auxiliary support Active Duty personnel and Military Chaplains worldwide, and veterans here at home in the United States. Our organization's motto is "For God, For Country, For Home". Posts and Auxiliaries can often be found attending Mass together on Veterans Day, Memorial Day, volunteering in VA Hospitals and supporting parish and veterans activities during the year.

Website: www.cwv.org
Contact #: 703-549-3622
Area of Service: National

CAMO CHALLENGE ASPEN

Challenge Aspen Military Opportunities (CAMO) provides adaptive therapeutic recreation and wellness experiences for military personnel diagnosed with cognitive and/or physical disabilities. CAMO offers an opportunity for veterans, their spouses/partners and caregivers to reconnect with outdoor recreation activities through professional adaptive instruction for summer and winter sports. CAMO encourages participants to attend one summer and one winter retreat so they can be exposed to one or more activities that may open the door to continued health and wellness.

Website: https://challengeaspen.org/military/
Contact #: 970-300-3396
Area of Service: National

CHALLENGED ATHLETES FOUNDATION

CAF's Operation Rebound program strengthens the mental and physical well-being of veterans, military personnel and first responders with permanent physical injuries by providing them opportunities to use sports and fitness to re-integrate into our communities and by empowering them through sports.

Website: https://www.challengedathletes.org/programs/operation-rebound/
Contact #: 858.866.0959
Area of Service: National

COHEN VETERANS NETWORK

The Cohen Veterans Network, Inc., a not-for-profit philanthropic organization, was created to serve them by providing high-quality, accessible, and integrated mental health care. Through our client-centered, customized outpatient care, we support veterans and their families as they begin their next mission: healthy and happy lives.

Website: www.cohenveteransnetwork.org
Contact #: 210-399-4838
Area of Service: National

DAVID LYNCH FOUNDATION

In 2005, we started the David Lynch Foundation for Consciousness-Based Education and World Peace to ensure that every child anywhere in the world who wanted to learn to meditate could do so. Now, the Foundation is actively teaching TM to adults and children in countries everywhere. How are we able to do it? Because of the generosity of foundations and philanthropists and everyday people who want to ease the suffering of others—and who want to help create a better world. If you don't already meditate, take my advice: Start. It will be the best decision you ever make.

Website: https://www.davidlynchfoundation.org/veterans.html
Contact #: 212-644-9880
Area of Service: National

EOD WARRIOR FOUNDATION

The EOD Warrior Foundation (EODWF) serves the EOD community by providing financial assistance and support to Active-Duty, Reserve and National Guard, Retired and Veteran EOD technicians and their families. Their support includes financial assistance and additional services such as morale events, peer-to-peer support, educational programs, connections to resources, care of the EOD Memorial, and sustained contact with EOD warriors and their families. The Foundation believes that the EOD family is for life. Their ongoing mission is to disarm the challenges of the EOD family by providing our support with compassion and caring to every individual we serve.

Website: www.eodwarriorfoundation.org
Contact #: 850.729.2336
Area of Service: National

FIDELCO GUIDE DOG FOUNDATION FOR MILITARY DOGS

Fidelco Guide Dog Foundation, Inc. is dedicated to limitless potential — to ensuring men and women who are blind enjoy increased independence to improve their lives and the world around them.

Website: www.fidelco.org
Contact #: 860.243.5200
Area of Service: National

FREEDOM SERVICE DOGS OF AMERICA

At Freedom Service Dogs, they unleash the potential of dogs by transforming them into custom-trained, life-changing assistance dogs for veterans in need.

Website: www.freedomservicedogs.org
Contact #: 303.922.6231
Area of Service: National

GIVE AN HOUR

Give an Hour's mission is to develop national networks of volunteers capable of responding to both acute and chronic conditions that arise within our society. By harnessing the skill and expertise of volunteer professionals, we are able to increase the likelihood that those in need receive the support and care they deserve. Give an Hour is honored to provide help and hope to those in need through a range of services and programs. They encourage potential participants to explore their initiatives and programs to learn more about some of the important work they are doing in communities across the country.

Website: https://giveanhour.org/initiatives-and-programs/
Contact #: info@giveanhour.org
Area of Service: National

HIGHER GROUND

As a positive and visible fixture in the adaptive sports industry, Higher Ground programs give individuals with disabilities the opportunity to experience recreation and the outdoors without limitations.

Website: https://highergroundusa.org/programs/#military
Contact #: (208) 726-9298
Area of Service: National

HOPE FOR THE WARRIORS

Hope For The Warriors believes those touched by military service can succeed at home by restoring their sense of self, family, and hope. Nationally, Hope For The Warriors provides comprehensive support programs for service members, veterans, and military families that are focused on transition, health and wellness, peer engagement, and connections to community resources.

Website: www.hopeforthewarriors.org
Contact #: 877.246.7349
Area of Service: National

INJURED MARINE SEMPER FI FUND

The Semper Fi Fund provides direct financial assistance and vital programming for combat wounded, critically ill and catastrophically injured service members and their families during hospitalization and recovery.

Website: www.semperfifund.org
Contact #: 760-725-3680
Area of Service: National

INTRANSITION

The Psychological Health Center of Excellence (PHCoE) was first established in 1995 as the Gulf War Health Center at Walter

Reed Army Medical Center, with a mission to care for Gulf War veterans with war-related physical and mental health challenges. That same year the Department of Defense (DoD) instituted the Comprehensive Clinical Evaluation Program (CCEP) to provide systematic clinical evaluations for the diagnosis and treatment of conditions connected to service in the Gulf War. The Gulf War Health Center developed the tertiary treatment component of the CCEP, a three-week specialized care program for veterans with medically unexplained physical symptoms. The program focused on individual and group therapy, patient education, physical and occupational therapy, and alternative medicine.

Website: www.pdhealth.mil/resources/intransition
Contact #: 800-424-7877
Area of Service: National

JEWISH WAR VETERANS OF THE USA

The Jewish War Veterans sends packages, generally of toiletries and kosher food items to those who are serving in Iraq, Afghanistan, and other places of conflict throughout the globe. They also supply special foods and ritual items for those celebrating the Jewish holidays on the battlefield abroad and at home.

Website: https://www.jwv.org/
Contact #: 202-265-6280
Area of Service: National

MILITARY VETERAN PROJECT

The mission of the Military Veteran Project is to prevent military suicides through research and treatment. 100% of every donation will allow a veteran to receive a treatment for military suicide prevention not available for immediately accessible by the VA or DOD.

Website: www.militaryveteranproject.org
Contact #: 785-409-1310
Area of Service: National

MISSION 22

Mission 22 is a non-profit who combats the ever-rising veteran suicide rate. Every day, more than twenty veterans are lost to suicide. Mission 22 wants to bring that number to zero. It does this with three main programs; veteran treatment programs, memorials and national awareness. Mission 22 provides treatment programs to veterans for Post-Traumatic Stress, Traumatic Brain Injury and other issues they might be facing.

Website: https://www.mission22.com/home
Contact #: (503) 908-8505
Area of Service: National

NEADS

In 1969, the Association was founded by a handful of military wives who wanted to make sure their widowed friends were properly taken care of. Two short years later, the Survivor Benefit Plan became law, and the Association has been hard at work ever since. A small, but determined, group of spouses around a kitchen table has expanded into a strong force of military families representing all ranks and services.

Website: www.militaryfamily.org
Contact #: 703.931.6632
Area of Service: National

NATIONAL MILITARY FAMILY ASSOCIATION

In 1969, the Association was founded by a handful of military wives who wanted to make sure their widowed friends were properly taken care of. Two short years later, the Survivor Benefit Plan became law, and the Association has been hard at work ever since. A small, but determined, group of spouses around a kitchen table has expanded into a strong force of military families representing all ranks and services. NMFA has, for 50 years, proven to stand behind service members, their spouses, and their children. The Association is a crucial source for government officials and key decision makers when they want to understand the issues facing our families. Through the support and programs they provide, and their voice on Capitol Hill and with the Departments of Defense and Veterans Affairs, the Association always looks out for the families who stand behind the uniform and for those who serve.

Website: www.militaryfamily.org
Contact #: 703.931.6632
Area of Service: National

NEW DIRECTIONS FOR VETERANS

The Cohen Veterans Network, Inc., a not-for-profit philanthropic organization, was created to serve them by providing high-quality, accessible, and integrated mental health care. Through our client-centered, customized outpatient care, we support veterans and their families as they begin their next mission: healthy and happy lives.

Website: ndvets.org
Contact #: 210-399-4838
Area of Service: National

PUPPIES BEHIND BARS

Puppies Behind Bars (PBB) trains prison inmates to raise service dogs for wounded war veterans and first responders, as well as explosive-detection canines for law enforcement.

Website: www.puppiesbehindbars.com
Contact #: 212.680.9562
Area of Service: National

SALUTE MILITARY GOLF ASSOCIATION (SMGA)

The Salute Military Golf Association's mission is to provide rehabilitative golf experiences and family inclusive golf opportunities for post 9/11 wounded war veterans in an effort to improve the quality of life for these American heroes. Eligible veterans include those wounded or injured in post 9/11 military operations, including those with Post-Traumatic Stress Disorder (PTSD) and/or Traumatic Brain Injury (TBI).

Website: smga.org
Contact #: (301) 500-7449
Area of Service: Regional–DC, NY, VA, MA, RI

TRINITY OAKS

The return from combat is an emotional roller coaster for our veterans. Adapting to life back home, many dealing with injuries internal and external, is a process made easier by spending time outdoors. Active participation in the outdoors is a powerful, healing, and fundamentally life-changing experience. Trinity Oaks' mission is to use hunting, fishing and outdoor activities to give back and make a meaningful difference on the lives of others.

Website: https://trinityoaks.org/veteran-programs/
Contact #: 210 447 0351
Area of Service: Regional–San Antonio, Texas

UNITED THROUGH READING

United Through Reading (UTR) was founded in 1989 by the wife of a Naval flight surgeon who deployed to Vietnam leaving his infant daughter at home. When the surgeon returned home, his little girl didn't know him and he had to re-enter her life as a stranger. The founder was a reading specialist and knew firsthand the importance of exposing children to literature from birth. Thus, a powerful concept emerged. Now, 30 years later, UTR still stands strong — and proven deployment after deployment. More than two million military mothers, fathers, aunts, uncles, older siblings, and children have sustained bonds and fostered literacy by sharing stories across even the greatest distances.

Website: unitedthroughreading.org
Contact #: (858) 481-7323
Area of Service: National

VALOR RUN

For as long as this country has been fighting wars, at home or abroad, women have been injured and killed in combat zones. Valor Run honors those women, now 161, who made the ultimate sacrifice in Iraq and Afghanistan as well as the families they left behind.

Website: www.valorrun.org
Contact #: valorrun@valorrun.org
Area of Service: Regional–Virginia

YELLOW RIBBON FUND, INC

The Yellow Ribbon Fund is a veteran service organization providing housing, transportation, and caregiver & family support to severely wounded, ill and injured post-9/11 servicemembers from every branch of the United States military following unexpected medical crises. Since their founding in 2005, their priority at Yellow Ribbon Fund has been to keep families together during the recovery process for wounded, ill, and injured service members. They do this by providing housing and transportation during recovery and by giving caregiver support when and where it is needed. They take our mission seriously, and it shows in the way they run their organization.

Website: yellowribbonfund.org
Contact #: 240-223-1180
Area of Service: National

DISABLED VETERANS NATIONAL FUND

The Disabled Veterans National Foundation (DVNF) provides critically needed support to disabled and at-risk veterans who leave the military wounded—physically or psychologically—after defending our safety and our freedom.

Website: DVNF.org
Contact #: (202) 737-0522
Area of Service: National

JAN STEPHENSON'S CROSSROADS FOUNDATION

Our mission is to provide our disabled veterans and first responders with the tools they need to move forward in life. Golf allows them to challenge themselves both mentally and physically which results in a stronger mind, body and spirit.

Website: janscrossroads.org
Contact #: 727-784-7606
Area of Service: National

BRIAN BILL FOUNDATION

The Brian Bill Foundation's Warrior Healing Program begins with individual four day therapeutic retreats for Special Operations Forces, active duty, veterans and their spouses who have been deployed since 911 and as a result have mild traumatic brain injuries, combat post traumatic stress and chronic pain. Our Warrior Healing Program includes the opportunity to learn about and try cutting edge therapeutic modalities such as Equine Assisted Learning, Accelerated Resolution Therapy, yoga, meditation, breathing techniques, iRest and nutrition. The retreats are for eight warriors or six couples focused on a team-centric approach, made up of those who share common backgrounds and experiences. These factors are key to the Warrior Healing Program's success, as is the fact that participation is confidential.

Website: www.brianbillfoundation.org
Contact #: (941) 840-4204
Area of Service: National

OPERATION HEALING FORCES

The mission of Operation Healing Forces (OHF) is to serve the needs of our active-duty and recent-veteran wounded, ill, and injured Special Operations Forces (SOF) and their spouses by starting or continuing the process of mentally, physically and emotionally healing in preparation to return to the fight or transition successfully into civilian life. Provides quality housing for displaced families going through extended medical care. They will provide private tours for Active Duty Military and veterans, upon request. Very compelling.

Website: operationhealingforces.org/home
Contact #: (727) 221-5071
Area of Service: National

U.S. ADAPTIVE GOLF ASSOCIATION

Serving the special needs community through their inclusion in the game of golf, including but not limited to access, instruction, and competition at all levels providing a competitive pathway.

Website: usaga.org
Contact #: 630-455-6018
Area of Service: National

Speciality and Social Services

*"For what avail the plough or sail,
or land or life, if freedom fail?"
–Ralph Waldo Emerson*

ACADEMYWOMEN

AcademyWomen is a global leadership and professional development organization that empowers aspiring, current and past women military leaders through mentoring, training, and growth opportunities to impact positive change locally, nationally and globally. Additionally their eMentor program: open to all veterans and provides an online continuum of support.

Website: www.academywomen.org
Secondary website: www.ementorprogram.org
Contact #: (888) 476-6112
Area of Service: National

AMERICAN VETERANS & STUDIES CENTER

The mission of the AVSC is to guard the legacies and honor the sacrifices of all American veterans. Through oral history preservation, educational programs and civic events, the AVC preserves the stories—and lessons—of veterans past and present, from which future generations can learn.

Website: www.americanveteranscenter.org
Contact #: (703) 302-1012
Area of Service: National

BLINDED VETERANS ASSOCIATION

National Blinded Veterans Association Auxiliary (BVAA) was established in 1977 to educate and offer assistance to friends and family members of blinded veterans. BVAA seeks to strengthen the spirit of fellowship that naturally exists among its members. Any friends, family members, or individuals age 18 and over who are interested in helping blinded veterans are eligible for membership.

Website: www.bva.org
Contact #: 800-669-7079
Area of Service: National

CELL PHONES FOR SOLDIERS

Cell Phones For Soldiers is a national nonprofit organization dedicated to providing cost-free communication services and emergency funding to active-duty military members and veterans.

Website: www.cellphonesforsoldiers.com
Contact #: (678) 580-1976
Area of Service: National

CAMO CHALLENGE ASPEN

Challenge Aspen Military Opportunities (CAMO) provides adaptive therapeutic recreation and wellness experiences for military personnel diagnosed with cognitive and/or physical disabilities. CAMO offers an opportunity for veterans, their spouses/partners and caregivers to reconnect with outdoor recreation activities through professional adaptive instruction for summer and winter sports. CAMO encourages participants to attend one summer and one winter retreat so they can be exposed to one or more activities that may open the door to continued health and wellness.

Website: https://challengeaspen.org/military/
Contact #: 970-300-3396
Area of Service: National

CHALLENGED ATHLETES FOUNDATION

CAF's Operation Rebound program strengthens the mental and physical well-being of veterans, military personnel and first responders with permanent physical injuries by providing them opportunities to use sports and fitness to re-integrate into our communities and by empowering them through sports.

Website: https://www.challengedathletes.org/programs/operation-rebound/
Contact #: 858.866.0959
Area of Service: National

HELP HEAL VETERANS

Help Heal Veterans (HEAL VETS) has provides free therapeutic craft kits to hospitalized and homebound veterans. We've helped traumatized veterans improve their motor skills, while also developing better feelings of self-esteem and self-worth. Our kits help veterans take their minds out of the past and off their pain, letting them live more in the present.

Website: www.healvets.org
Contact #: (951) 926-4500
Area of Service: National

HONOR FLIGHT NETWORK

Honor Flight Network seeks to transport America's Veterans to Washington, DC to visit those memorials dedicated to honor the service and sacrifices of themselves and their friends.

Website: www.honorflight.org
Contact #: 937-521-2400
Area of Service: National

HUD-VASH VOUCHERS

The Departments of Housing and Urban Development-Veterans Affairs Supportive Housing (HUD-VASH) program combines Housing Choice Voucher (HCV) rental assistance for homeless Veterans with case management and clinical services provided by the Department of Veterans Affairs (VA). VA provides these services for participating Veterans at VA medical centers (VAMCs) and community-based outreach clinics.

Website: https://www.hud.gov/program_offices/public_indian_housing/programs/hcv/vash

Contact #: (202) 708-1112
Area of Service: National

KOREAN WAR VETERANS ASSOCIATION, INC.

The Korean War Veterans Association seeks to provide travel accomodation to veterans of the Korean War.

Website: kwva.us
Contact #: (217) 345-4414
Area of Service: National

LUKE'S WINGS

Luke's Wings was founded in January 2008 by a group of compassionate individuals who observed the struggles of wounded warriors at Walter Reed Army Medical Center, now Walter Reed National Military Medical Center, in Washington, DC. From January 2008 through 2011, Luke's Wings operated as a strictly volunteer based charity. There were no salaries, no full time employees, and no office space; just passionate volunteers making a difference. However, that all changed in 2012 when sufficient funding allowed for three full time employees; ultimately growing into the organization it is today. After ten years, we now serve a long list of military medical facilities, VA medical centers and hospice facilities across the country and have provided airfare for families across all 50 states and internationally. Though far from our humble beginnings, our team of five full-time employees remain committed to maintaining a clear and obvious mission: to support the community of wounded, ill and injured service members and their loved ones with the gift of flight. Join us in our mission to keep our families flying!

Website: www.lukeswings.org
Contact #: (202) 735-5382
Area of Service: National

MERCY MEDICAL ANGELS

Mercy Medical Angels mission is to remove the barrier to medical care. They provide transportation on the ground and in the air to clinical care for those in need. More than 17,000 free trips to medical care are provided each year, ensuring that no one in need is denied medical care because they don't have transportation.

Website: mercymedical.org
Contact #: (757) 318-9174
Area of Service: National

NAVY CLUB OF THE UNITED STATES

On 18 June 1938, at a Navy Veterans Reunion in Quincy, Illinois, a new and powerful organization, the Navy Club of the United States of America, was launched. On that day, a Constitution and By-Laws was adopted to govern this unique and distinguished group, speaking the language of the men who go down to the sea in ships. The original organizational committee drew up a broad administrative charter that envisioned a new concept in collectively bringing together the many private Navy Clubs and Navy Veteran Organizations that had sprung up across the country, and by so doing, give each member and prospective member, a powerful voice as a Nationally Recognized Organization.

Website: navyclubusa.org
Contact #: (585) 967-4935
Area of Service: National

NAVY MUTUAL AID ASSOCIATION

The Navy Mutual Aid Association was established on July 28, 1879, during a meeting of U.S. Navy officers at the Navy Department in Washington, D.C. to better assist members of their service during financially difficult times. Today Navy Mutual assists servicemembers and their families in securing the federal benefits to which they may be legally entitled, as well as to educate servicemembers and their families on matters of financial security. Navy Mutual offers an array of insurance and other health benefits to qualified members of the military and retirement communities.

Website: www.navymutual.org
Contact #: (800) 628-6011
Area of Service: National

OPERATION GRATITUDE

Every year, Operation Gratitude sends 250,000+ individually-addressed care packages to Soldiers, Sailors, Airmen and Marines deployed overseas and to their children left behind. Also, to New Recruits, Veterans, First Responders, Wounded Heroes and their caregivers.

Website: www.operationgratitude.com
Contact #: 800-651-8031
Area of Service: National

PARALYZED VETERANS OF AMERICA

Paralyzed Veterans of America, a congressionally chartered veterans service organization founded in 1946, has developed a unique expertise on a wide variety of issues involving the special needs of our members—veterans of the armed forces who have experienced spinal cord injury or dysfunction.

Website: www.pva.org
Contact #: (866) 734-0957
Area of Service: National

SOLDIERS' ANGELS

Soldiers' Angels has a 96.5% Efficiency Rating and has become one of the highest rated nonprofits in the country. The mission of Soldiers' Angels is to provide aid and comfort to the men and women of the United States Army, Marines, Navy, Air Force, Coast Guard, their families, and a growing veteran population. Thousands of Soldiers' Angels "Angel" volunteers assist veterans, wounded, deployed personnel, and their families in a variety of unique and effective ways. In 2018 alone, Soldiers' Angels provided over $25 million in aid to over 515,000 service members, veterans, wounded heroes, and military families. Through the Deployed Support Programs, combat deployed service members were supported with 28,659 care packages and 177,307 letters. The Veteran Support Program served over 24,600 veterans with food assistance and handed out over 39,995 items bedside to patients in VA Hospitals across the country. Through the seasonal holiday Adopt-A-Family program, Soldiers' Angels volunteers "adopted" 1,637 military families, that included 2,882 military children. New and expectant spouses of combat deployed as well as active-duty female service members were provided 1,165 baby boxes to help them welcome their new bundles of joy. Soldiers' Angels volunteers are the heart of the organization and logged over 164,524 volunteer hours just in 2018!

Website: soldiersangels.org
Contact #: 210-629-0020
Area of Service: National

VETERANS CONSORTIUM PRO BONO PROGRAM

The Veterans Consortium Pro Bono Program (Pro Bono Program) was created with a dual mission: to provide assistance to unrepresented veterans or their family members who have filed appeals at the U.S. Court of Appeals for Veterans Claims (Court); and to recruit and train attorneys in the then fledgling field of veterans' law.

Website: www.vetsprobono.org
Contact #: (888) 838-7727
Area of Service: National

VETERANS HEALING FARM

Veterans Healing Farm's mission is to serve our nation's veterans by growing and donating high-quality fruits, vegetables, and flower bouquets to veterans and their caregivers free of charge. Additionally, we support veterans by offering workshops on innovative gardening techniques and foster a thriving micro-community of veterans and civilians who build deep friendships and cultivate emotional, physical, and spiritual health.

Website: www.veteranshealingfarm.org
Contact #: 828-606-8212
Area of Service: Regional–North Carolina

THE INDEPENDENCE FUND

The Independence Fund prides itself on working with great organizations, and great people, to help accomplish our goals in creating new lives for wounded Veterans and their Caregivers. We are very thankful for all of the assistance provided by all of our partners and sponsors over the last decade, and looking forward to continued collaboration!

Website: independencefund.org
Contact #: 888.851.7996
Area of Service: National

OPERATION FINALLY HOME

Operation FINALLY HOME was established in 2005 as a non-partisan/nonprofit 501(c)(3) organization and has already had a significant impact across the country. To date, we have over 250 home projects completed or in planning in 33 states providing custom-built, mortgage-free homes to America's military heroes and the widows of the fallen, those who have worn America's uniform and sacrificed so much to defend our freedoms and values. While we are very proud of the work we have been able to do, we are keenly aware that there is much more to be done.

Website: operationfinallyhome.org
Contact #: (806) 441-5712
Area of Service: National

THE JOURNEY HOME PROJECT

Often when our veterans return from their tour of service, the tolls of war have been too great to bear alone. Wars in the Middle East and other parts of the world have left some of our bravest service personnel with injuries that will affect them the rest of their lives. The horrors of war leave psychological scars that make it difficult to reenter civilian life. The Journey Home Project sees as its mission connecting donors to veterans' organizations that do the most good.

Website: thejourneyhomeproject.org
Contact #: See website
Area of Service: National

JAN STEPHENSON'S CROSSROADS FOUNDATION

Our mission is to provide our disabled veterans and first responders with the tools they need to move forward in life. Golf allows them to challenge themselves both mentally and physically which results in a stronger mind, body and spirit.

Website: janscrossroads.org
Contact #: 727-784-7606
Area of Service: National

U.S. ADAPTIVE GOLF ASSOCIATION

Serving the special needs community through their inclusion in the game of golf, including but not limited to access, instruction, and competition at all levels providing a competitive pathway.

Website: usaga.org
Contact #: 630-455-6018
Area of Service: National

JOB OPPORTUNITIES FOR DISABLED VETERANS

Disabled person, Inc. is a 501(c)(3) charitable organization whose mission is to reduce the high unemployment rate of individuals and veterans with disabilities. They do this by offering classes teaching coding skills based on the latest tools and technologies. They additionally offer courses in microsoft, sharepoint and other digital suites. Lastly they offer coursework for in-demand skills in IT administration and cloud platform solutions.

Website: jofdav.com
Contact #: (760) 420-1269
Area of Service: National

Transition Services

"Treat the civilian world as a foreign country. They speak a different language, have a different culture and different customs. Adapt to the new country by adapting to the language, culture and customs."

–GENERAL JIM MATTIS (RET.)

AIR WARRIOR COURAGE FOUNDATION

The Air Warrior Courage Foundation was formed by military aviators to "care for our own." The organization works closely with the Red River Valley Fighter Pilots Association to do that by focusing on active duty, guard, reserve and retired military personnel and their families needing financial assistance for medical, educational, and other extraordinary expenses not covered by other military, veterans', or charitable institutions.

Website: www.airwarriorcourage.com
Contact #: (877) 921-2923
Area of Service: National

AMERICAN LEGION

The American Legion is a nonpartisan, not-for-profit organization focused on mentoring youth and sponsorship programs as well as transition services for transitioning and recently transitioned members of the armed forces.

Website: legion.org
Contact #: (800) 433-3318
Area of Service: National

AMVETS NATIONAL SERVICE FOUNDATION

The American Studies Center (ASC) provides professional help to veterans applying for compensation and benefits from the VA, offered at no charge. The ASC also offers thrift stores around the country for veterans. These stores offer clothes, household goods and more. Eligible veterans can apply for scholarships through the ASC website.

Website: amvetsnsf.org
Contact #: (301) 459-6181
Area of Service: National

DISABLED AMERICAN VETERANS

Disabled Veterans of America provides free, professional assistance to veterans and their families in obtaining benefits and services earned through military service and provided by the Department of Veterans Affairs (VA) and other agencies of government. In addtion they assist with outreach concerning its program services to the American people generally, and to disabled veterans and their families specifically.

Website: www.dav.org
Contact #: 859-547-3382
Area of Service: National

FLEET RESERVE ASSOCIATION

Fleet Reserve Association is first and foremost a community of the Sea Services; U.S. Navy, Marine Corps, and Coast Guard personnel. Your enlisted service in any of these branches—past or present, for a short time or for the long haul—is your passport to membership in an association that works hard for you and your family on Capitol Hill and in your local community. FRA's guiding principles are Loyalty, Protection and Service to our shipmates. The FRA offers assistance to members in managing VA applications as well as offering scholarship money for undergraduate and graduate schooling.

Website: www.fra.org/fra/Web/FRAHome
Contact #: 703-683-1400
Area of Service: National

GARY SINISE FOUNDATION

The Gary Sinise Foundation was established under the philanthropic direction of a forty-year advocate for our nation's defenders, actor Gary Sinise. Each of the Foundation's programs originated from Gary's personal relationships with our nation's service community and a wide range of nonprofits he had supported for decades. Ever aware of the gaps of care these deserving heroes often encounter, he was inspired to serve them—always giving a little more. With the creation of the Gary Sinise Foundation, his crusade now supports all those who sacrifice on our behalf: active duty, veterans, first responders, and their loved ones. Each program shows appreciation for America's heroes through entertainment, family support, and acts of gratitude. At the Gary Sinise Foundation, they serve our nation by honoring our defenders, veterans, first responders, their families, and those in need. They do this by creating and supporting unique programs designed to entertain, educate, inspire, strengthen, and build communities.

Website: www.garysinisefoundation.org
Contact #: (888) 708-7757
Area of Service: National

HOPE FOR THE WARRIORS

Hope For The Warriors believes those touched by military service can succeed at home by restoring their sense of self, family, and hope. Nationally, Hope For The Warriors provides comprehensive support programs for service members, veterans, and military families that are focused on transition, health and wellness, peer engagement, and connections to community resources.

Website: www.hopeforthewarriors.org
Contact #: 877.246.7349
Area of Service: National

INJURED MARINE SEMPER FI FUND

The Semper Fi Fund provides direct financial assistance and vital programming for combat wounded, critically ill and catastrophically injured service members and their families during hospitalization and recovery.

Website: www.semperfifund.org
Contact #: 760-725-3680
Area of Service: National

IRAQ AND AFGHANISTAN VETERANS OF AMERICA

Iraq and Afghanistan Veterans of America (IAVA) is a veterans advocacy and support organization. They seek to connect, unite, and empower more than 400,000 veterans and allies nationwide. Founded by an Iraq veteran in 2004, IAVA is the non-partisan leader in advocacy, public awareness and 1-on-1 case-management support. They aim to organize locally, and drive impacts nationally.

Website: www.iava.org
Contact #: 202-544-7692
Area of Service: National

MILITARY OFFICERS ASSOCIATION OF AMERICA (MOAA)

The Association works to lobby Congress and other parts of the government on behalf of active, reserve and retired officers working to highlight the value and impact of the officer community across all branches of the US military.

Website: www.moaa.org
Contact #: (800) 234-6622
Area of Service: National

NATIONAL VETERANS FOUNDATION

The National Veterans Foundations provides crisis management, information and referral needs of all U.S. Veterans and their families through: management and operation of the nation's first vet-to-vet toll-free helpline for all veterans and their families. They also offer public awareness programs that shine a consistent spotlight on the needs of America's veterans in addition to providing outreach services that provide veterans and families in need with food, clothing, transportation, employment, and other essential resources.

Website: www.nvf.org
Contact #: (310) 642-0255
Area of Service: National

NATIONAL VETERANS LEGAL SERVICES PROGRAM

In the wake of World War II, the U.S. Congress enacted laws that continue to stand as a solemn promise to every citizen who steps forward to serve our country in military uniform: if you are injured or become permanently disabled due to your military service, the federal government will care for you and your family for the rest of your life. Since the beginning, the National Veterans Legal Services Program (NVLSP) has worked to ensure that the government delivers to our nation's 22 million veterans and active duty personnel the benefits to which they are entitled because of disabilities resulting from their military service to our country.

Website: www.nvlsp.org
Contact #: 202.265.8305
Area of Service: National

NAVY SEAL FOUNDATION

Since the attacks of Sept. 11, 2001, there has been an unprecedented demand for our Special Operations Forces. Never before has so much been asked of so few, from so many, for so long. Established in 2000 to serve U.S. Navy SEALs, Special Warfare Combatant-craft Crewmen, Naval Special Warfare support personnel and their families, the Navy SEAL Foundation's programs are focused on the preservation of the Naval Special Warfare force and their families. They provide a comprehensive set of programs specifically designed to improve health and welfare, build and enhance resiliency, empower and educate families and provide critical support during times of illness, injury, loss and transition.

Website: www.navysealfoundation.org
Contact #: 757.744.5326
Area of Service: National

NAVY-MARINE CORPS RELIEF SOCIETY

The Navy Marine Corps Relief Society is dedicated to providing educational services to active, reserve and retired members of the military. They also seek to provide aid in times of disaster and emergency funding in the event of a qualifying personal event.

Website: www.nmcrs.org
Contact #: (800)-654-8364
Area of Service: National

OPERATION HOMEFRONT

Operation Homefront is a national nonprofit whose mission is to build strong, stable, and secure military families so they can thrive — not simply struggle to get by — in the communities they have worked so hard to protect. For over fifteen years, we have provided programs that offer: RELIEF (through Critical Financial Assistance and transitional housing programs), RESILIENCY (through permanent housing and caregiver support services) and RECURRING FAMILY SUPPORT programs and services throughout the year that help military families overcome the short-term bumps in the road so they don't become long-term chronic problems. Operation Homefront has consistently earned high ratings from leading charity rating services, including Charity Navigator, which gave OH 4 Stars for 11 consecutive years for superior service and accountability. At Operation Homefront, 92 percent of expenditures goes directly toward delivering programs and services to the military families who need it most.

Website: www.operationhomefront.net
Contact #: (210) 659-7756
Area of Service: National

OPERATION SUPPORT OUR TROOPS—AMERICA

The mission of Operation Support Our Troops-America is to support the morale and well-being of American forces by providing comfort, resources and education to them and their families both while they are deployed in harm's way and after their return.

As a volunteer based non-profit organization, they provide the opportunity for our community members to express their appreciation and offer support for our troops. Engaged in the longest war of our country's history and with our servicemen and women completing multiple tours of duty, we are committed to showing them that "We Have NOT Forgotten."

Website: www.osotamerica.org
Contact #: (630) 971-1150
Area of Service: National

The Military Order of the Purple Heart
The Order seeks to foster an environment of goodwill and camaraderie among combat wounded veterans, promote patriotism, support necessary legislative initiatives, and most importantly, provide service to all veterans and their families.

Website: www.purpleheart.org
Contact #: (703) 642-5360
Area of Service: National

SWORDS TO PLOWSHARES

Founded in 1974 by veterans, Swords to Plowshares is a community-based not-for-profit 501(c)(3) organization that provides needs assessment and case management, employment and training, housing, and legal assistance to roughly 3,000 veterans in the

San Francisco Bay Area each year. We also advocate on behalf of veterans and provide community education for over 1,500 first responders, employers, social workers, attorneys, and other professionals who engage with veterans. The Department of Veterans Affairs provides healthcare and benefits to a percentage of veterans, but depends on community partners, including Swords to Plowshares, to fill in the gaps and meet the needs of those who have served. Our community comes together to deliver local, comprehensive services to meet the needs of our veterans.

Website: www.swords-to-plowshares.org
Contact #: (415) 252-4788
Area of Service: Regional- California, The Bay Area

THE MISSION CONTINUES

The Mission Continues is a national, nonpartisan nonprofit that empowers veterans to continue their service, and empowers communities with veteran talent, skills and preparedness to generate visible impact.

Website: missioncontinues.org
Contact #: (314) 588 8805
Area of Service: National

THE TRANSITION HOUSE INC.

The Transition House, Inc.'s Veterans Program is designed to engage homeless veterans and guide them towards independence through employment and permanent housing using the Veterans Administration Grant and Per Diem funding. They offer services to male veterans, and our facility can host 40 male veterans at a time. This program is for veterans that may or may not have been involved with the judicial system and those with disabilities.

Website: thetransitionhouse.org/transform-your-life/veteran-programs
Contact #: 407-892-5700
Area of Service: National

TRAGEDY ASSISTANCE PROGRAM FOR SURVIVORS

TAPS offers compassionate care and resources to all those grieving the loss of a military loved one. Since 1994, TAPS has provided comfort and hope 24/7 through a national peer support network and connection to grief resources, all at no cost to surviving families and loved ones. TAPS provides a variety of programs to survivors nation and worldwide. Their National Military Survivor Seminar and Good Grief Camp has been held annually in Washington, D.C., over Memorial Day weekend since 1994. TAPS also conducts regional survivor seminars for adults and youth programs at locations across the country, as well as retreats and expeditions around the world. Staff can get you connected to counseling in your community and help navigate benefits and resources.

Website: www.taps.org
Contact #: (800) 959-8277
Area of Service: National

TRAVIS MANION FOUNDATION

The Travis Manion Foundation strives to unite and strengthen communities by training, developing, and highlighting the role models that lead them. They develop programs, training opportunities, and events designed to empower veterans and families of the fallen, and then inspire them to pass on their values to the next generation and the community at large.

Website: www.travismanion.org
Contact #: (215) 348-9080
Area of Service: National

TREA: THE ENLISTED ASSOCIATION

The mission of TREA: The Enlisted Association is to enhance the quality of life for uniformed services enlisted personnel, their families and survivors–including active components, Reserves, and National Guard, and all retirees; to stop the erosion of earned benefits through our legislative efforts, to maintain our esprit de corps, dedication and patriotism, and to continue our devotion and allegiance to God and Country.

Website: trea.org
Contact #: (303) 752-0660
Area of Service: National

USA CARES

USA Cares is committed to its mission to provide financial and advocacy assistance to post-9/11 active duty U.S. military service personnel, veterans and their families. USA Cares was launched through a grassroots partnership between WAVE-3 TV in Louisville, KY, the Mid-South Division of Kroger Food Stores, and the Association of the United States Army Fort Knox Chapter. The organization was dubbed Kentuckiana Cares, with a goal to raise funds to help military families in financial crisis through the sale of "Support Our Troops" yard signs. In October 2003, in response to the increasing number of requests for assistance, Kentuckiana Cares evolved into what is now USA Cares, a national non-profit organization that has assisted thousands of veterans and military families facing hardships related to service.

Website: usacares.org
Contact #: 800-773-0387
Area of Service: National

THE INDEPENDENCE FUND

The Independence Fund prides itself on working with great organizations, and great people, to help accomplish our goals in creating new lives for wounded Veterans and their Caregivers. We are very thankful for all of the assistance provided by all of our partners and sponsors over the last decade, and looking forward to continued collaboration!

Website: independencefund.org
Contact #: 888.851.7996
Area of Service: National

AMERICA'S WARRIOR PARTNERSHIP

From city to city and town to town across America, there is no one organization or platform to ensure each unique veteran is holistically supported or that each veteran service organization has access to the national resources they need. America's Warrior Partnership is filling these gaps between current veteran service organizations: bolstering efficacy, improving results, and empowering initiatives. America's Warrior Partnership is the connection that brings local veteran-centric nonprofits together through coordination and collaboration, ensuring consistent information is obtained, relevant services are provided, and national resources are utilized. We attack inefficiency and amplify the work of established nonprofits and government agencies. America's Warrior Partnership is truly a force multiplier for warrior care that enhances communities where great Americans choose to live and contribute. Our ultimate goal is to create a better quality of life for all veterans by empowering local communities to proactively and holistically serve them.

Website: americaswarriorpartnership.org
Contact #: (706) 434-1708
Area of Service: National

LEAD THE WAY

Through their Ranger Assistance Programs they address and support the ongoing needs of the Rangers and families beyond what the government can offer. They work directly with the U.S. Special Operations Care Coalition to assist U.S. Army Rangers. Rangers are among the most disciplined and skilled Warriors in the world and they are dedicated to helping them utilize their ingrained skills by empowering them to thrive in careers and at top Universities around the country. When Rangers make the decision not to re-enlist in the Regiment after a long and successful military career, the transition back to civilian life can be challenging. Through their Transition Programs, we are committed to helping their Rangers through the reintegration process, ensuring that they achieve their goals of a rewarding and prosperous civilian life.

Website: www.leadthewayfund.org
Contact #: 516-439-5268
Area of Service: National

OPERATION HEALING FORCES

The mission of Operation Healing Forces (OHF) is to serve the needs of our active-duty and recent-veteran wounded, ill, and injured Special Operations Forces (SOF) and their spouses by starting or continuing the process of mentally, physically and emotionally healing in preparation to return to the fight or transition successfully into civilian life. Provides quality housing for displaced families going through extended medical care. They will provide private tours for Active Duty Military and veterans, upon request. Very compelling.

Website: operationhealingforces.org/home
Contact #: (727) 221-5071
Area of Service: National

About the Author

JENNIFER HAMMOND is a high energy and versatile woman who not only serves as a real estate executive; but also as a SiriusXM satellite radio talk show host, a best-selling author, and is a member of The Happiness Hall of Fame!

As a Vice President of TTR Sotheby's–one of the country's leading luxury real estate companies–she has helped numerous clients attain their dreams in real estate for over 22+ years. Jennifer is a licensed realtor in Maryland, Virginia and Washington DC. She is a real estate investor and is passionate about helping others become knowledgeable about being successful as a real estate investor.

Jennifer has helped make the world a better place by educating, inspiring and empowering people by hosting The Jennifer Hammond Show on SiriusXM for almost 10 years, and has aided thousands of veterans and their families in finding the help they need through her best-selling book "101+ Resources for Veterans" first edition. Jennifer is excited to help more Veterans and their families with this second edition.

To learn more, visit: www.jenniferjhammond.com